EQUINE-IMITY

Equine-imity

Stress Reduction and Emotional Self-Regulation in the Company of Horses

Qigong for Somatic Horsemanship

Beverley Kane, MD

Dreamspark Press

Design by Meadowlark Publishing Services.

Cover art montage by Judith Ogus.

Published by Dreamspark Press.

Manufactured in the United States of America.

ISBN 978-0-578-75115-3

Published 2021

To my beloved Ruben

CONTENTS

Introduction

When the grass looked greener at a Fortune 500 company, Allison left her comfort zone at the top of her game as editor of a small food magazine. But at the first meeting in her new corporate boardroom, she felt the threat of being laid low (or perhaps too high) by the Peter Principle of rising ever upward until you fail. Her performance anxiety was so severe that it was *somaticized*—expressed through her body—as a rapid heartbeat that sent her to the emergency room. The cardiologist found nothing abnormal with Allison's physiological heart. He diagnosed her as having a stress response, a condition of the emotional "heart." Weeks later, still experiencing "heart" symptoms, Allison came to the Wisdom of the Mare, an equine experiential learning program for women in transition. This somatic horsemanship workshop used interactions with gentle horses as a way to counteract the stress that comes from life's major changes.

What Is Somatic Horsemanship?

Somatic horsemanship is the practice of exploring the physical relationship between humans and horses, on the ground and on the horse, in order to promote physical, emotional, mental, and spiritual health in both species. While all these aspects of the horse-human relationship are interrelated, for most horses the most tangible means of interacting is through the five senses and the body as a whole.

Somatic means *of the body.* Somatics as a mind-body conditioning and healing practice began with the work of the late Thomas Hanna, a student of Ukrainian-Israeli engineer and physicist Moshe Feldenkrais. The story goes that Feldenkrais used his understanding of electrical currents in mapping out the circuitry of the nervous system to rehabilitate a sister who had suffered brain damage. He then pioneered his eponymous movement therapy to reprogram the brain following strokes and for other neurological disorders. As with the Feldenkrais Method, Hanna Somatics emphasizes small, slow, isolated movements to heal injuries, correct anatomical abnormalities, and promote healthy aging in nerves, muscles, and joints. Somatic horsemanship uses these principles in teaching deep breathing; slow, simple muscle movements; and mindful activities with horses to tap into mind-body states of health, peace, and strength.

My relationship with my body became redefined in middle age. At fifty, I realized I was no longer twenty-five. Although I remained healthy, my body was noticeably, well … older. Long work hours, business travel, and expense account dinners conspired to thwart my attempts to stay fit. I had also lost the spiritual connection to my body that came from the discipline of sports and adherence to a healthy diet. Once a marathon runner, mile-a-day swimmer, and solo wilderness backpacker, I began to notice a decline in speed, strength, flexibility, and stamina. I was always an animal lover, and I found myself attracted to horses as magnificent beings who could become extensions of my body.

Who Moved My Cheese?

When the dot-com bust hit Silicon Valley at the turn of the millennium, I was working as a doctor-patient communication expert at WebMD. As the company began pulling its Sunnyvale operations, about fifty of us chose to take a hefty severance package rather than move to New York or Atlanta. Our managers solemnly paraded us into private rooms one by one to confirm the rumors and give us our walking papers. I thought, *No big deal, I'm A-OK*. Twenty minutes later, my true state of mind became evident when I drove a few blocks from the office to put gas in my car. Subconsciously more shaken up than I wanted to admit, I drove off with the gas nozzle still attached to my car, pulling the hose out of the pump.

I immediately began some frenzied mental machinations to plan how to find my next job. With an epidemic of closures and layoffs hitting the Valley, the book *Who Moved My Cheese?* by Dr. Spencer Johnson made the rounds. It was a kiddie-style allegory about two mice and two humans—and two types of reactions to having the rug pulled out from under them. One type remains stuck looking for the same old cheese; the other type moves on creatively.

My close friend Sheri, also a physician, sat in the garden with me while I poured out my feelings of stress and woe. After patiently listening to my lamentations, she asked, "So, what do you really want to do?"

The first thing that came to mind was, "Well, I've been wanting to take riding lessons."

I decided to do this one small thing for a while instead of obsessing on my lost cheese.

Dreams and Dream

Guided by what Swiss psychiatrist and mystic Carl Jung called a Big Dream, a nighttime dream of cosmic proportions, my riding extended into the practice of equine-assisted learning and psychotherapy, and finally into somatic horsemanship.[1] My first horse was aptly and synchronistically named Dream. In intimate, whole-body contact with this big, beautiful animal, I regained my sense of the physical. I felt Dream's flesh and bone as part of me, felt us as eachother's[2] centaur-like appendages, joined at the body and at the heart.

One year after the dot-com bust, I established my private practice, Horsensei Equine-Assisted Learning & THerapy (HEALTH). My services were dedicated to teaching career and social skills to corporate employees, university staff, and medical professionals. These programs emphasized the psychological and pragmatic aspects of the horse-human relationship in modeling communication, teamwork, and leadership. The somatic aspects played a lesser role.

Then, in the spring of 2011, I got bucked off a step stool in my kitchen. I sustained a fractured foot, a dislocated right elbow, and a sprained left wrist. If I were a horse, I'd have been called three-legged lame!

My orthopedic surgeon told me not to ride for three months. Not ride?! Now, most physicians know little about horseback riding. When a doctor tells you not to pursue a sport, you must consider where the advice is coming from.

1   *Red Mustang Stallions Dancing in the Desert.* In Carey, Michiko Akahori. *Women's Meaningful Dreams: The Treasure Within the Feminine Psyche.* Doctoral dissertation. Institute of Transpersonal Psychology. Palo Alto, CA. 24 May 2010. https://pqdtopen. proquest.com/doc/597937273.html?FMT=ABS

2   I use the single word *eachother* to denote Oneness among beings.

Is she just expressing generic caution about potential risks? Or has she identified specific biomechanical limitations in your body that preclude that particular activity? In my case, it was the former. I was physically able to ride but would not have tolerated another accident. So I decided to compromise: I enrolled as a client at the National Center for Equine Facilitated Therapy, a premier hippotherapy (physical therapy on horseback) and therapeutic riding facility. Riding, which I had always done holding the reins and usually in a saddle, was now done bareback and out of my control. Someone led the horse, another person was a side walker, and Corie Thompson, my inspirational therapeutic riding instructor, directed my movements. (Corie would later help create Equine-imity and become my first co-facilitator.) My entire focus was on how my body felt on top of the horse. Instead of the nervous, gotta-do-it-right attitude I carried into my riding lessons, here I was just another kid. We played the airplane game with my arms straight out. We played 'round the moon where I turned in my seat 360 degrees. These tearfully joyous sessions brought home the message that for me, the entry point to mind-body-spirit wholeness has always been the physical body. And the physical and metaphysical embodiment of wellness is the horse.

I continue to experience body and mind revitalization best when sitting atop a horse, but also when I am grooming, massaging, and breathing with horses, or just watching them in pasture. All these activities evoke feelings of strength, grace, balance, and peace. To make these benefits accessible to others through contact with horses, I offer the Equine-imity somatic horsemanship program to reduce stress, dispel negative emotions, support graceful aging, and renew a spiritual connection with nature and one's happy place within it.

A proliferation of yoga and horsemanship programs, mainly for equestrians, has grown out of the popularity of yoga in corporate, college, and community wellness centers. Other somatic horsemanship programs use *tai ji*, Mindfulness-Based Stress Reduction, and the equine-assisted implementations of body-oriented psychotherapies such as Eye Movement Desensitization and Reprocessing (EMDR) and Somatic Experiencing.

Why Horses?

Horses are consummate teachers of healthy embodiment and emotional resiliency. Unlike our family dogs and cats, horses are not housebroken. They are not conditioned to feel shame and guilt for their biological functions. Cats and dogs are predators who create stress for other animals. Horses are prey animals who run to safety, then let go of fear when the danger has passed. They have survived for 60 million years by becoming more adept than their attackers at sensory awareness and emotional self-regulation. After being acutely stressed into a flight response, horses quickly recover and go back to grazing—their baseline *equanimity*. We learn from horses how to go from a state of hyperarousal, due to uncontrolled emotions such as anger, grief, and fear, to a state of peace.

Weighing up to 2,200 pounds, horses are the great equalizers of all people fat and thin, weak and strong, young and old. Anyone can feel light, powerful, youthful, and athletic beside or astride a horse.

Somatic horsemanship is one of many equine-assisted activities and therapies (EAAT), which include equine-assisted learning and psychotherapy, hippotherapy, and therapeutic riding. Scientific evidence is mounting for the benefits of these programs.

Why Qigong?

Equine-imity teaches the art of just *being* and the art of *doing* slowly and mindfully. The core of Equine-imity's doing aspect is the practice of *qigong* (chee goong). Qigong is an ancient Chinese healing exercise with slow, graceful movements suitable for people of all ages and physical abilities. It is the most gentle, most traditionally health-oriented form of East-meets-West moving meditation.

Unlike sitting meditation, qigong doesn't ask us to stay rigidly immobilized with blank minds. Unlike yoga, qigong doesn't entail pretzel poses or head-down contortions. Unlike kung fu, aikido, and karate, qigong is non-combative, requires minimal strength and fitness, and results in almost no injuries. Qigong is the ideal technique for teaching humans to go back to grazing.

Equine-imity uses one of the best known and simplest forms of medical qigong, the *Ba Duan Jin* (literal translation, "eight sections of brocade"; poetic translation, "eight silken movements"). Medical studies of the Ba Duan Jin show its unique healing benefits. In the modified Shaolin Ba Duan Jin set that we practice, five of the eight classical forms can be done on horseback. We call these the *Wu* (five) *Duan Jin* and learn them initially on the ground, then on the horse.

The qigong movements prepare you for blending your *ch'i* (qi) life force energy with that of your horse. This mindful contact between your two bodies allows the human heart, with its rate of up to 120 beats per minute during times of stress, to slow to a normal 60 to 80 beats per minute by *entraining* it with the horse's heart, with its resting rate of 40 beats per minute.

When Allison shared a dan tien ch'i hug with the mare Bella, the racing feeling in her chest subsided for the first time in weeks. The moment Allison exhaled into her dan tien lower abdominal energy center, Bella let out a huge, whuffling sigh of release. You will learn the dan tien press and the dan tien hug in chapter 13, *Con Su Permiso*, and you will learn to treasure the whuffle.

Why Somatics?

Equine-imity has at its foundation the practice of balancing the four functions described by Carl Jung: intellect, emotion, sensation (somatics), and intuition. In Western culture, stress is caused mainly by an overwrought intellect manifesting as worry and self-criticism and by runaway negative emotions such as anger, fear, guilt, envy, and sadness. The key to creating equanimity lies in cultivating positive behaviors based on healthy somatic and intuitive—including spiritual—attitudes and practices. We use the term *somato-spiritual* to mean the combination of body and soul that creates health and happiness in a deeply meaningful, even sacred, way.

What Can Equine-imity Somatic Horsemanship Do for You?

- Do you suffer from stress that manifests as bodily symptoms such as headaches, stomach aches, or insomnia?

- Do you feel a disconnect between your work, family, or social life and who you are, or wish to be, most deeply and idealistically as a person?
- Are you seeking a harmonious integration of your intellectual, emotional, physical, and religious or spiritual activities?
- Are you in transition or at a crossroads where merely thinking, talking, and worrying about problems and options has failed to create clear solutions?
- Do you suspect that there are subtle energies, coincidences, and hidden meanings in life that are not fully described in or predicted by the scientific, academic, or business world?

If the answer to any of those questions is yes, you can benefit from an approach that uses the wisdom of the body and the intuition, as taught by horses, to create health, wholeness, and balance in your life. For while horses are not highly developed verbally and intellectually, they are geniuses of somatic, instinctual, and emotional functioning.

What You Will Learn in This Book

Written for the not-necessarily-equestrian, not-necessarily-qigong-y reader, *Equine-imity* offers:
- A reappraisal of the human body as beautiful no matter what its size or shape
- Horses as models of embodiment and teachers of physical, emotional, and spiritual health
- Stories of horses healing humans

- Seven simple, easy-to-follow medical qigong exercises
- Applied principles from exercise physiology and sports medicine, natural horsemanship, and equine-assisted psychotherapy
- The Stanford Equine-imity four phase somatic horsemanship program, proven to reduce stress
- Resources for how to locate horses within half an hour of your home or work
- Resources for how to pursue equine-assisted activities and therapies as a career
- A heartfelt appeal to keep horses appreciated, valued, and employed

Equine-imity is for those who have, or have had, horses and for those who have never even touched a horse. It is for anyone in middle age or older who wishes to become reinvigorated by the power, grace, and majesty of the horse. *Equine-imity* is also for younger generations, who, studies show, cope more poorly with stress than older generations. Teens and young adults can use *Equine-imity's* principles of sports medicine, martial arts, natural horsemanship, and meditation for sports and school challenges.

Equine-imity does not attempt to make you into an equestrian or a qigong master, although if either of those happens as a result of its activities, your life will be much richer for it. But you can use the teachings far beyond any experience with horses and qigong.

This book teaches you how to return to, or find for the first time, a place of invigorated peace and health. It helps you keep finding it, and keep returning to it, even without horses or structured exercises.

Equine-imity is divided into four parts.

Part I introduces you to the nature of horses—why they are so well suited to teach us how to reduce stress and let go of damaging emotions. Horses live in their bodies differently from the way we, our cats, and our dogs do. You will learn important ways in which horses are different from our household pets.

Part I also examines the evidence for a sixth sense in horses and humans. When doing somatic horsemanship activities, it is important to be aware of all influences coming into play. We present evidence that, according to landmark work by parapsychologist Dean Radin, PhD, bodies can, independent of the mind, precognitively sense a variety of stimuli.

Part II gives you a look at some historical and cultural views of the human body. Many religious and esthetic traditions make it difficult for us to appreciate our bodies as a source of pride and pleasure and as the key to stress reduction. Part II also looks at the science of stress physiology and psychology as it relates to the qigong forms in Part III. Westerners accustomed to partaking of their philosophy and their science in separate bowls will see how these ingredients can be combined into one recipe for living.

Part III teaches you how to orchestrate the body's subtle energy systems in coordination with your breathing and muscle movement. You will learn the Wu Duan Jin qigong forms, plus some techniques from yoga, mindfulness meditation, and Reiki, preparatory to practicing them with, and sometimes on, a horse.

Part IV shares the entirety of our Stanford Equine-imity program, allowing you to experience some or all of the activities under the supervision of an experienced, trustworthy horse person.

It is fine to skip the background material and go right to

the techniques and activities in Parts III and IV. Later you can go back and read the rest of the book while sitting in a lawn chair beside your new horse friend.

Don't know how to meet a horse? In the back of the book, appendix C gives you resources and suggestions for finding equine-assisted activity programs or private individuals with horses in your area.

A not-at-all-hidden agenda of *Equine-imity* is to teach appreciation of horses, the land they live on, and the trails they walk. In writing this book, I visualized all of you and all of the horses who will be enriched, and perhaps saved, by your engagement with eachother.

Our bodies are our temples and horses lead us to the altar.

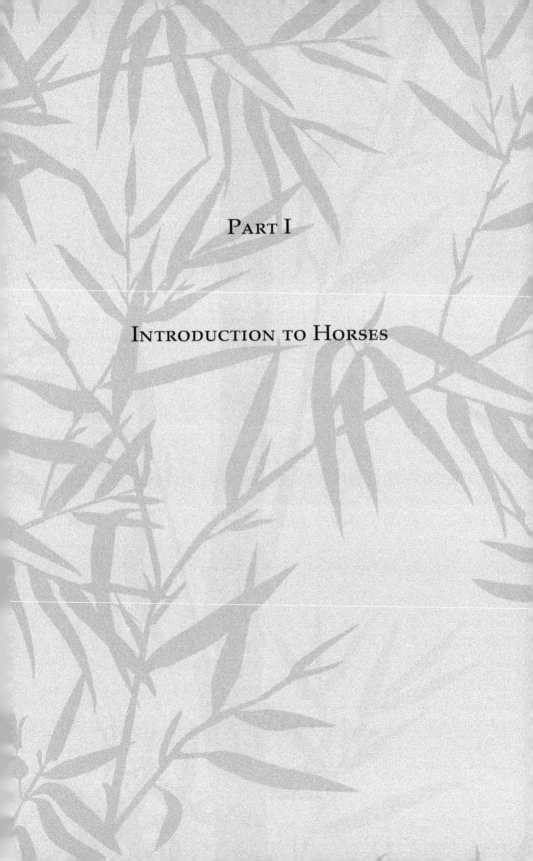

Part I

Introduction to Horses

1

Happiness Is a Warm Horse

Why Horses?

Why are horses ideal for teaching us how to live better? How have we come to see these intelligent, sensitive creatures as facilitators of all aspects of human development? A big part of their value for us is the way in which they can react to minute changes in our moods, behaviors, and body language, offering us constant feedback for our actions and internal states. In speaking of horses as psychological, emotional, or somatic beings, any divisions we make among those qualities are ultimately artificial and arbitrary. We make these distinctions only to emphasize the horse's unique contribution to our appreciation of the somatic dimension of our integrated selves.

Horse Psychology

Unlike our family cats and dogs, who evolved as predators and are now highly domesticated, horses evolved as prey

animals and remain essentially feral even in the captivity of
our barns and pastures.[1]

Horses are social creatures who readily and honestly
respond to the challenges inherent in forming and sustaining
relationships. Horse herds have an established, but often
labile, hierarchy that is tested several times a day to reconfirm
that the healthiest, most able horse—who might be the smallest one—can continue to lead the herd and ensure its survival.
Dominance among horses is both situation dependent and
non-transitive.[2] That is, some horses are dominant around
food, some around a patch of real estate in the shade, some
around monopolizing people, some around their love interests
or buddies. In my horse's herd, I witnessed a non-transitive
hierarchy where Rainy was dominant to Cody and Cody was
dominant to the rest of the herd, but Lokin and a few others
submissive to Cody were dominant to Rainy.

With horses, what they see is what you get. Their physical
actions are consistent and congruent with their thoughts and
emotions. Incongruency occurs in humans when our outward
expressions don't match our inner thoughts and feelings.
Many horses are uncomfortable with our incongruencies.
Although horses don't cognitively formulate the statement
"This human is incongruent," they can become agitated by the
palpable tension we exude in repressing our emotions and by

1   The Western Hemisphere has no "wild" horses. Proto-horses
     originated in Wyoming, USA, 60 million years ago, and were
     the size of a fox. They became extinct after the last ice age, 10,000
     years ago. Equines now living in the Americas are descended
     from those who were introduced by, and escaped from, fifteenth-
     century Spanish explorers and missionaries such as Cortez,
     Ponce de Leon, and Coronado. These once domesticated horses
     are termed "feral." The last remaining species of true wild horse
     is the Przewalski (sha-vahl'-skee) horse of Mongolia.
2   Glossary terms appear in brown on first use in the text.

the confusion we create with our conflicting requests, mixed messages, and indecisiveness. Most horses are fine with our crying into their manes; they are not fine with our putting on a happy face while we are crying inside. Although horses can be patient and forgiving, faced with our incongruency or lack of leadership, they will take matters into their own hooves, ignoring or avoiding us in order to feel safe and sure. We gain their trust and cooperation when we are congruent and able to display clear, consistent intent.

Horse Emotions

Horses are naturally curious, but seeing an unfamiliar or unexpected object triggers the survival instinct. Horses fear anything they perceive as a bodily threat until it is proven to be otherwise. A typical response to a strange stationary object is evasion or cautious approach-and-retreat behavior, often accompanied by snorting and hopping. When surprised by a moving object like a flapping tarp or a bird flying out of the brush, horses may shy, spook, or run until safety can be re-established. Then, after being temporarily panicked, horses quickly forget about the incident and regain their equanimity. Rather than hold on to trauma or analyze it to death, horses go back to grazing as if nothing happened. The back-to-grazing principle is one of the key teachings from horses.

As part of their need for inner-outer congruency, horses abide our emotional extremes, as long as we don't express such extremes abusively. Even when we relate to them with emotions that are displaced from our other relationships—a dynamic called transference—horses remain unperturbed. Hence we cherish their ability to tolerate our mental and physical projections, as well as our emotional transference.

Horse Physiology—Horses as Models of Embodiment

Horses are the epitome of embodiment in the Buddhist sense of the body as the earthly manifestation of the soul. Their sheer size and the magnitude of their movements evoke our heightened awareness. They live in states of intense sensuality—eating, running, excreting, mating—without guilt or shame. Horses put us back in our bodies by showing us how completely and comfortably they live in theirs.

Since the horse is a prey animal in the wild, her life depends upon her sensory, and likely extrasensory, acuity. Survival requires attunement to all stimuli in her environment—smells, sights, noises, and tiny skin perturbations. Horses can feel a fly land on their backs. They can smell water in the desert from miles away. They can see, with visual fields totaling roughly 357 degrees (see drawing), the flick of a herd mate's ear out of the corner of their eye. They sense the difference between our leaning one shoulder toward them or away from them. Horses have a highly developed ability to discern changes in the stance and arousal levels of other herd members, an ability they easily transfer to interactions with human beings.

Horses motivate us to slow down and relax. They help us transfer the hyperactivity—the "energy"—of our minds toward our lower bodies and the ground. A resting horse has a heart rate of 35 to 40 beats per minute. An anxious human has a heart rate of 80 to 110 or more. With the dan tien press and the dan tien hug described in chapter 13, the human heartbeat can *entrain* with that of the horse. This unconscious synchronization of heart rates slows the human's heart and causes her to feel more relaxed.

Horses can also energize and strengthen us. Watching a

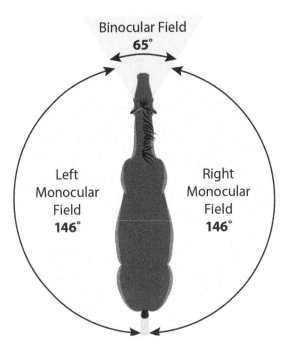

Binocular Field
65°

Left
Monocular
Field
146°

Right
Monocular
Field
146°

horse gallop and rear up in play, we are infused with stamina and power and joy. We feel especially invigorated when they carry us on their backs in a ground-covering trot or canter.

As we will see in chapter 10, Postures, Points, Powers, and Gestures, horses have big energy centers that are anatomically analogous to our own. When we blend our energy centers with the horse, body-to-body, there is an intimate exchange of movement, flow, and shared potency. Part of the conventional wisdom about why little girls love horses is that it is so empowering for a 60-pound child to partner with a 1,000-pound animal.

Horses who live outdoors in fields and forests teach us about our connection with nature. They awaken within our cellular memory a time when we, too, lived simply on the earth. The revival of nature-based therapy seeks to rescue us from the ills of traffic, smog, and sick building syndrome and restore us to health. "Healthy as a horse" means following the example of horses who live naturally on the land.

By interacting with horses somatically, emotionally, and psychologically, we deepen our awareness of personal issues and core feelings, and increase our ability to reach our true potential. We learn how to establish boundaries, blend energy centers, and direct a large creature, and therefore ourselves and our lives, by using mental focus, clarity of intent, and somatic blending. These skills have far-ranging applications for satisfaction in social relationships, careers, and parenting. And you will have the opportunity to discover that for yourself as you put this book's principles into practice.

2

ORIGINAL GRACE, ORIGINAL GRAZE

Back to Grazing

Emotions are like wild horses.

—Paulo Coehlo, *Brida*

ody, my high-energy, high-strung Arabian gelding, spied a life-threatening form coming toward him at a gallop—the dreaded, deadly, horse-devouring white plastic grocery sack carried on the wind. After doing the "Arab teleport"—a quantum leap with no intermediate states—to land ten feet away from the bag, he realized it was not going to hurt him.

Oh, he shrugged. *No big deal. I'll just grab some more grass.*

This return to baseline equine-imity after a fright is characteristic of horses. Horses do not hang on to episodic trauma, unrealized threats, and temporary upsets the way we do. They are *conservative.* That is, their survival as prey animals who rely on flight depends on their ability to conserve energy for running, should the danger prove to be real. They do not waste energy on situations that prove harmless. Unless the potential menace becomes an actualized calamity, horses quickly go "back to grazing."

Grazing is not necessarily eating. Horses can graze for hours as a way to relax. The horses we brought to the Stanford Wellness Faire grazed on the lawn continuously for six hours, largely ignoring the hay we laid down. For them, nibbling on the sparse grass was an anti-stress activity for coping with hundreds of horse-selfie-seeking faire-goers and the Stanford marching band. Grazing is like a pacifier for a baby. In adult humans, the same purpose is served by stress eating, chewing gum or tobacco, and smoking.

Can you think of something about which you have built up worry, fear, anger, jealousy, sadness, or resentment that you would like to let go of? The qigong postures, gestures, and forms you will learn in later chapters will teach you to release these unpleasant accumulations and to go back to grazing.

3

MIRROR, MIRROR ON THE GRASS

Archetypes, Projections, and Mirror Neurons

arch is the most beautiful month of the year in Northern California. The hills are Glocca Morra green. Bright yellow mustard flowers grow high as a foal's eye along the San Francisquito Creek in the oak-studded forty-acre pasture that is my office. This is a much touted nature therapy environment where clients come for their private Equine-imity somatic horsemanship *sessions.*

On this warm, sunny morning, Lara, a pediatrics resident, walks in front of me on the narrow path to the upper pasture. We are headed to the field that is predictably the 10 a.m. grazing stop for the horses in their daily migration over the hills and through the copses. Just weeks earlier, Lara had what she termed a mental breakdown during her twenty-four-hour shift in the neonatal intensive care unit. With the fatalism of a late twenty-something, and with not-fully-formed medical knowledge, Lara diagnosed herself as psychotic, ADHD (attention deficit hyperactivity disorder), clinically depressed, and autistic. Her psychiatrist is in fact medicating her for at least one of those conditions. Remembering her happy childhood with ponies, she has come to somatic horsemanship for relief from her (and her doctor's) psychopathological view of herself and her body's reasonable reaction to the sleep-deprived rigors of medical training.

As we come into the visual, auditory, and olfactory field of the ten horses dotting the hillside, I invite Lara to simply observe the herd. After several minutes, I ask her to relate what she is seeing. Immediately, Lara begins talking about each horse in turn—what each is thinking and feeling, and why he or she is behaving in a certain way.

Thus begins the process of projection: attributing our internal qualities to people, animals, and objects such as inkblots that exist outside ourselves. Simple observation of the horses and the free flow of projections onto them are important first steps in somatic horsemanship. Playing with projection frees our minds of subconscious material that gets in the way of reducing stress. This chapter describes two types of projection, psychological and somatic, that help us relate to horses and relate horses back to ourselves. In order to work with our projections and the strong emotions that signify their presence, we must first understand archetypes.

Archetypes and Somarchetypes

Archetypes from the Psyche

Archetype (Greek *arche*, "origin or beginning," and *type*, "form" or "pattern") is the term used by Carl Gustav Jung (1875–1961) to refer to the blueprints for the human psyche that exist across all cultures, throughout time, in every individual. Archetypes are the straight-from-Central Casting roles that each society enacts according to its own customs and prejudices: loving mother, wise elder, beautiful princess, knight in shining armor, evil fiend, god and goddess, innocent baby animal.

The entire cast of archetypes performs inside the theater of every human mind, usually after waiting in the wings. Each of us can potentially express every archetype. Myths, folk legends, and fairy tales—remarkably similar across all languages and cultures—are stories built around archetypal themes. Archetypal dramas come to us in literature, in mass media, and in dreams. We also see them in waking dreams, starkly symbolic events that seem to just happen to us: in our triumphs, tragedies, lucky breaks, accidents, and illnesses.

The primary Jungian archetypes are Persona (my public self), Anima and Animus (my gender-complementary, yin-and-yang-balancing love interest), Dark Shadow (my enemy), Bright Shadow (my idol), Trickster (my blunders and accidents), the Hero, the Divine Child (Horus and Baby Jesus), and Willing Sacrifice (Christ and other martyrs). In myth and folk legend, whether idolized as Pegasus or demonized as the Kelpie, Horse is both a psychological archetype and, as we shall see, a somatic archetype.

The Warrior Archetype

As a subtype of both Hero and Willing Sacrifice, the Warrior archetype deserves special mention because it has been so often associated with Horse and depicted on horseback. From Genghis Khan and Alexander the Great to medieval knights to cowboys and American Indians, from *The Iliad* to *The Lord of the Rings* to *War Horse*, the Horse Warrior evokes bravery, honor, purpose, and glory. Images of combat both antagonize us with their violence and inspire us with their displays of courage. Many battle legends in which the physical body is sacrificed imply the afterlife of an eternal soul. As he led his war party on horseback, Lakota Sioux Chief Crazy Horse cried, "Hokahey [let's go]! Today is a good day to die!" The Lakota and other plains tribes have a strong belief in an after-death Happy Hunting Ground where game is plentiful and the white man cannot go.

In Search of the Warrior Spirit, by ex-Marine and aikido master Richard Strozzi-Heckler, describes his training of United States Special Forces (Green Berets and Navy SEALs) and other top-flight troops. In teaching aikido to military service people, Strozzi-Heckler infuses the warrior spirit in a nonlethal, non-hateful way. For many years, he conducted classes in the Middle East that included Israelis and Palestinians blending energy—the meaning of ai-ki-do—with eachother. He describes the nature of the true warrior when war was a more gallant, hand-to-hand, horse-to-horse combat. He contrasts those crusades with those in the news today, fought impersonally with machine guns, planes, bombs, missiles, drones, and IEDs that additionally kill innocent civilians. My personal experience with Richard has shown that our respective practices of qigong and aikido share many of the same somatic, philosophical, and spiritual teachings.[1]

---

1   Richard is also the originator of Strozzi Somatics and the Strozzi Institute for Embodied Leadership. The institute's methodology involves eliciting an individual's or organization's defining values and introducing practices that combine conceptual understanding with physical activity to foster behaviors that accord with those values. Many of the practices are based on aikido. Strozzi Somatics was a founding principle of SkyHorse Equine Guided Education, established by Ariana Strozzi Mazzucchi. (See appendices C and D.)

Modern wars, and the politics that provoke them, show failure of whole societies to integrate the true Warrior spirit. Extremes of both hawks and doves are eachother's Dark Shadow. Warmongers and terrorists, fueled by hatred, use their armies for Dark Shadow hostilities. The vociferous, self-righteous pacifist (in contrast to the less incendiary peace activist) is also unable to integrate the Warrior. She often has Dark Shadow issues with even healthy aggression, like the assertiveness needed to support her goals and defend her personal boundaries. From left, right, or center, the emotional vehemence of one ideology against the other is the hallmark of Dark Shadow. One of the Wu Duan Jin forms in chapter 11, The Wu Duan Jin, promotes healthy expression of the Warrior archetype by releasing the ch'i of anger and drawing in the ch'i of tolerance and compassion.

Somatically oriented activities such as ropes courses, paintball fights, and contact sports also afford relatively safe, healthy expression of the Warrior. CodeWarrior is an amusing name for a software development environment that suggests assimilation of this archetype into geek culture.

The Jungian quaternity of elements making up the Four Ways of Wisdom described in chapter 5, Junger than Springtime, is illustrated by the Knights in tarot divination cards. From the most yin, receptive Knight of Cups to the most yang, aggressive Knight of Swords, the Knights are archetypes of the quest for the wholesome expression of the Four-Fold Wisdom: Cups: water, emotions; Pentacles: earth, somatics; Wands: fire, intuition; Swords: air, intellect. (See next page.)

According to Jung, one of our life goals is individuation, the process by which all the archetypes are integrated into the Whole Self. The Whole Self archetype is represented by mandala figures such as Tibetan tangkas and the Native

KNIGHT of CUPS. | KNIGHT of PENTACLES | KNIGHT of WANDS. | KNIGHT of SWORDS.

American Medicine Wheel. In common with the mystical traditions of world religions, individuation is achieved when we recognize the fundamental unity of all beings and all experience.

Projection—The Magic Mirror

To the extent that we have not embraced all the archetypes within our own psyches, we will forever project them outward

onto others. Archetypal projection is the act, usually unconscious, of attributing or blaming one's feelings, thoughts,
circumstances, and attitudes to or on other individuals, racial
or ethnic groups, or animals. Everything we experience as
other—external to ourselves—represents, in part, a projection of our internal states upon our mates, parents, children,
enemies, heroes, and animal companions. We project onto
others both characteristics that we admire and believe we lack
("Wizard of Oz thinking"), and characteristics that we despise
and have not yet come to terms with when we meet them in
ourselves. The magic mirror principle says, "What I see in you
is also in me; if what I see were not already in me, I would not
even recognize it in you." The folk concept of this principle
is "the pot calling the kettle black." A fundamental teaching
from the Hindu Vedas is *tat tvam asi*—thou art that (I am you).
Although in expression we are each unique, in essence we are
all the same and all part of the collective consciousness, or
the Divine. As equine-assisted psychotherapist Wyatt Webb
says, "You spot it, you got it!"

When our unconscious projections lead to hateful emotions, destructive behaviors, or dangerous infatuations, we
damage our relationships and ourselves.

Most projections are more or less true and valid. We project
intelligence onto Nobel Prize winners, evil onto people who
commit villainous acts, and strength, beauty, and majesty onto
beings such as horses who "objectively" have those qualities.
Just because it's a projection doesn't mean it isn't true, and if
something is true "objectively," it will draw projections out
of us like a magnet. The most reliable sign of projection is
a strong emotion, such as love or hate, that accompanies an
impression, observation, or judgment. Our emotional response
to an "objective" truth to which others are emotionally neutral

alerts us to the presence and strength of our projections. We take out what we put in.

When we read novels or watch movies, we can harmlessly project our archetypal roles onto the characters. Children do this quite playfully by becoming witches and butterflies and superheroes for Halloween. Video and role-playing games also allow players to revel in archetypal identities and activities.

In somatic horsemanship, we deliberately elicit projections. To avoid *premature closure*—biasing projections before they have a chance at expression—we don't even state the horses' names. We ask our participants to give the horse a new name, thus encouraging even stronger projections. In this way, the horse might become identified with the person herself, a family member, manager, or other key figure.

When asked which horse she wanted to connect with, Lara was immediately attracted to the big palomino. An unusual mustang-Belgian draft cross, he was the flashiest, most massive horse in the herd. When I asked her to name him, she blurted out, "Peter," the name of her chief resident. With the semi-unconscious, semi-automatic utterance of this name, Lara shared a secret: although she was engaged to her drug-abusing college sweetheart, she harbored an unexpressed crush on Peter.

Projections drawn out in this way lead to self-understanding. I invited Lara to commune with Peter the Horse out of my hearing. In doing so, she began to cry, and cleansed herself of thoughts and feelings she could not share with her fiancé, with Peter the chief resident, or with me—feelings that, left unspoken, contributed to her felt sense of breakdown.

Somarchetypes—Projections from the Body

Archetypes are *mental* constructs that press down like cookie cutters on the dough of our psyches. However, psychological archetypes are insufficient to describe all our projections, especially onto horses. Expressing our Inner Horse additionally requires projections from our bodies. We project onto horses our imagined sensations of size, strength, balance, grace, coordination, agility, speed, and stillness.

I have named projections from the physical body somarchetypes. Somarchetypal projection is the act, usually unconscious, of experiencing sensations from bodies outside our own. Combined with empathy and enabled by the action of mirror neurons, discussed in the next section, we see examples of somarchetypal projection with infectious yawning and with tactile sensations such as formication (with an "m"): the feeling of bugs crawling on us when we read about ants and spiders.

We project somarchetypes onto people, animals, plants, and inanimate objects. Monty Python's sketch "Romantic Interlude" shows a succession of visual clichés that represent sexual activity—fireworks, a time-reversed chimney collapse, a train going through a tunnel. Our laughter at these obvious metaphors is evidence of somarchetypal projection.

We project sensations of tallness and shortness, strength and weakness, skinniness and fatness, baldness and hairiness, even alternate genitalia, onto those who have these features. We can do this because these attributes are innate to the collective cellular unconscious of which our bodies are a part. We project our desirable, idealized Bright Shadow somarchetypes onto Olympic athletes, ballet dancers, and the Black Stallion. We project our feared and rejected Dark Shadow somarchetypes onto disabled or disfigured people, sick puppies, and clogged toilets. (The "Ewww!" emotion is a clue to Dark Shadow projection.) Did you ever urge your car on with your body? In my family, we pump our pelvises and chant "Up! Up! Up!" to get our little car over Tejon Pass in the Tehachapi Mountains. Somarchetypal projection again.

In the 1930s, the father of psychosomatic medicine, Edmund Jacobson, showed that just thinking of a specific task activates the muscles used in performing it.[2] Watching Lindsey Vonn schuss down a hill or watching a horse and rider jump a six-foot fence can stimulate the same body parts as performing the act ourselves.

Analogous to concepts of empathy, sympathy, and telepathy, we can postulate a somatopathic function of sensory perception that causes us to sense what others sense. Dance Movement Therapy uses just such a principle, called kinesthetic empathy, in body-oriented psychotherapy. If you've ever found yourself unconsciously tapping your foot to music, yawning when someone else yawns, or smiling when you hear laughter, you've experienced somatopathic projection or kinesthetic empathy.

Kinesthetic-predominant learners acquire new motor skills by feeling as if they are inside the bodies of those whom they observe performing the task. I do my best riding when I'm in the arena with Marie, an accomplished riding instructor with superb equitation whose body I can somatopathically emulate in a state of projective kinesthesia.

---

2   Jacobson E. Electrical measurements of neuromuscular states during mental activities. I. Imagination of movement involving skeletal muscle. *Am. J. Physiol.* 1930; 91:567-608.

As with mental archetypes, it is the strength of the emotional charge from the externally triggered sensation that tells us we're projecting—in this case, a somarchetype. Movie scenes running the gamut from G-rated hugs to XXX-rated pornography evoke somarchetypal body reactions accompanied by feelings of affection or erotic desire. We project both mentally and somatically onto horses who bite, kick, sass, and strike eachother. We tend to interpret those behaviors as hostile, and we may feel physically hurt and emotionally afraid or angry when we project onto horses interacting in this way. However, horses assign different meanings to these communications. They take things with none of the ego wounding and psychological overlay that we humans project onto physical aggression.

Analogous to the individuation process using psychological archetypes, we can theorize that our bodies have the potential to integrate every possible physical attribute and sensation. We can deliberately choose to project the somarchetypes that feel good and that contribute to our health and well-being. We do so when we look at horses and vicariously sense how they are enjoying their bodies.

Chiron, the Centaur—Archetype and Somarchetype

The mythical figure of the half human, half horse is the ultimate projective fantasy of the Horse somarchetype. The earliest images of the Centaur date back to Bronze Age Mycenaean pottery fragments around 1500 BCE. Both male centaurs and, later, female centaurs, the Kentaurides, have been described in Greek and Roman art and literature.

Centaurs, like the half man, half goat two-legged Satyrs, were mythologized for their animal-like passions and uncontrollable bouts of rowdiness, lust, and drunkenness. An exception was Chiron ("kye-ron"). Rejected by his parents and schooled in medicine by Apollo, Chiron was plagued with excruciating chronic pain from having been pierced in his thigh with a poison arrow accidentally shot by his friend Herakles. No longer able to tolerate the agony, Chiron traded his immortality to Prometheus for the gift of death. Death ended his physical suffering and granted him eternal peace in the southern sky as the constellation Centaurus.

Chiron Centaurus.

Chiron is the archetype of both Willing Sacrifice, similar to Christ figures, and the Wounded Healer. In 1977, astronomers detected the minor planet they named Chiron. This discovery led astrologers to assign to its placement in one's natal chart the nature and timing of our somatic ordeals, especially illnesses and accidents. In accordance with the myth of Chiron, these traumas can only be healed by the symbolic death of the portion of the ego that identifies with, and feels victimized by, the wounding. Somarchetypal projections of bodily death onto Chiron, soldiers, and daredevils prepare us for both psychic upheavals and physical setbacks and for our own eventual death and possible afterlife.

The story of my fall from the step stool, told in the introduction, was a classic Chiron drama. I had to accept the death of the part of my ego that was stuck in the psychological rather than somatic model of equine-guided learning.

Centaur mythology persists in the space age. On July 30, 2020, Ruben, a former NASA scientist, and I cheered the launch of the *Perseverance* Mars rover. *Perseverance* was launched with, and successfully decoupled from, the Centaur rocket, so named because it is the head and torso of the Atlas V launch system. Used in more than 250 space missions, Centaur is nicknamed "NASA's workhorse."

The Centaur archetype personifies—or horse-onifies—our concept of "healthy as a horse." It is a powerful image to hold when we watch or ride horses and borrow from them sensations of a strong body, peak athletic condition, and healthy aging. These perceptions can be attributed to somarchetypal projections from our muscles, bones, organs, glands, and nervous system—in fact, from every cell of the 37.2 trillion in our bodies.

Mirror Neurons

An intriguing possibility for the neurophysiological basis of somarchetypal projection lies in the network of so-called mirror neurons of the brain. A mirror neuron is a nerve cell that fires both when an animal acts and when he observes an action performed by another animal. Thus, the neuron *mirrors* the behavior of the other animal's neurons—monkey see, monkey do. Such neurons have been directly observed in nonhuman primates and other species, including birds.

Indirect evidence for the existence of mirror neurons in humans comes from magnetic resonance imaging (MRI) brain scans taken during observation and execution of motor tasks. Since an MRI does not show the activity of individual brain cells, we must draw conclusions from relatively large areas of the brain and from invasive experiments on vivisected animals.

There is sparse direct evidence for the existence of mirror neurons in humans. The best data we have were obtained from a piggyback study by Mukamel and colleagues at UCLA.[3] In a piggyback study, the interventions and data generated by the principal study are repurposed for a secondary study. In this case, the research subjects had electrodes already implanted in their brains to see whether they were candidates for surgical treatment of epilepsy. Mukamel's group was able to obtain data from these electrodes to look for evidence of mirror neurons.

In his study, participants were given laptop computers in their hospital beds. They were asked to alternately observe and perform various motor tasks on the laptops while EEG (electroencephalogram) activity was recorded from approximately 1,200 brain cells. In classifying the discharges from these cells, the investigators identified types of neurons that provide clues to how the perceptions of the actions of others enter into the motor abilities of the perceiver. The findings suggest that multiple areas in the human brain participate in the mirroring mechanisms that link perceptions of others to a person's own actions. We can imagine a scenario where, in seeing one horse groom another with her teeth, our brain centers involved in grooming become activated to learn the task. Our skin senses the skin of the horse being groomed. Our mouths sense the amount of pressure felt by both groomer and groomee.

Mirror neurons are not only implicated in processing others' tactile and motor experiences; they are also deemed

---

3   Mukamel R et al. Single neuron responses in humans during execution and observation of actions. *Curr Biol.* 2010; 20(8):750-6.

essential for recognition of others' emotional expressions.[4] A complex interplay of neurons and social context, as well as gender and individual differences, may explain the role of mirror neurons and other structures in mimicry, empathy, and the ability to walk a mile in somebody's moccasins. Correspondingly, "it has been postulated … that the inability of autistic children to relate to people and life situations in the ordinary way depends on a lack of a normally functioning mirror neuron system."[5]

We must be cautious about taking a reductionist view of mirror neurons or of any theory that claims the mind can be understood solely in terms of the brain. Important research in dreams, near-death experiences, out-of-body encounters, remote viewing, and intercessory prayer argues against an epiphenomenalist view of biology. Epiphenomenalism is the belief that conscious processes are the result—an *epiphenomenon*—of biochemical reactions in brain cells. However, in *Proof of Heaven* by Eben Alexander, MD, and *Erasing Death* by Sam Parnia, MD, PhD, people who were clinically unconscious were found to be aware of resuscitation efforts and other activities around them. Later, these comatose persons were able to identify members of their resuscitation teams who had not otherwise been involved in their care. I personally had such a patient, a plump and prosperous businessman in his sixties, when I was a medical student at the San Francisco Veterans Affairs Hospital. Because I was young and might have said something vaguely metaphysical, Mr. Katz confided

---

4   Bastiaansen JACJ, Thioux M, Keysers C. Evidence for mirror systems in emotions. *Phil. Trans. R. Soc. B.* 2009; 364:2391-2404.

5   Acharya S, Samarth S. Mirror neurons: Enigma of the metaphysical modular brain. *J Nat Sci Biol Med*. 2012; 3(2):118–124.

in me that he was out of his body during his cardiac arrest. He later went around to thank members of the code blue team, whom he had seen from above but had never met before or since.

Mirroring in Horses

In chapter 6, Whoa Nellie, Go Nellie, we note that pastured horses may acquire stall vices like cribbing and wind sucking when previously stall-kept horses who exhibit these stress behaviors are introduced into the herd. A horse may also panic upon seeing another horse running in fear. The reaction is so immediate, automatic, and forceful that many riders will quickly dismount when the shout "Loose horse!" goes up. A mounted horse who would ordinarily take direction from her rider might reflexively bolt upon seeing a terrified, running horse.

We must also ask whether horses mirror humans. Since mirror neurons are found in brain structures common to all mammals, it is probably safe to say that horses are capable of this behavior. Certainly we have seen cats and dogs who mimic chewing motions when they observe their people eating. Many horses will trot along at liberty with a person who is jogging, probably as a trained habit but possibly imitating on the basis of mirror neurons. The principle of kinesthetic empathy has been demonstrated in dogs[6] and postulated in horses during the formation of complex physical and emotional relationships in equine-assisted therapies.[7]

---

6   Shapiro K J. Understanding dogs through kinesthetic empathy, social construction, and history. *Anthrozoös*. 1990; 3(3):184-195.

7   Scopa C et al. Emotional transfer in human–horse interaction: new perspectives on equine assisted interventions. *Animals*. 2019; 9 (12):1030.

Mirror Neurons and Presentiment

As in the case of the amygdala, also noted in chapter 6, mirror neurons may fire before the conscious mind has registered the act that is being mirrored. At the Institute of Noetic Sciences in Petaluma, California, internationally respected parapsy-chologist Dean Radin, PhD, has shown that the sensorimotor body has a mind of its own. That is, he showed that the body responds to stimuli *before* they are initiated and long before, in microsecond eras, the conscious mind registers them.

In an elegant series of experiments,[8,9] participants were shown emotionally calming or neutral photos vs. emotion-ally provocative photos. Calm targets included photos of landscapes, nature, and people; emotional targets included erotic, violent, and accident scenes. Radin and his colleagues measured skin conductance in response to the images. This electrodermal activity is a measure of sympathetic nervous system (SNS) activity, as SNS stimulation increases sweating in the skin. As you may remember from high school chemistry class, electricity is conducted more easily through salt solu-tions like our sweat than on dry skin.

Remarkably, Radin showed that the participants' skin conductance increased an average of 5 to 6 seconds *before* an emotionally charged image was shown!

Radin termed this advance somatic knowing "presenti-ment"—the body's ability to sense stimuli before they are presented. Presentiment is like precognition. Precognition

---

8   Radin D. Electrodermal presentiments of future emotions. *J Sci Explor.* 2004; 18(2):253-273.

9   Radin D. Psychophysiological evidence of possible retrocausal effects in humans. Frontiers of Time: Retrocausation—Experi-ment and Theory. *American Institute of Physics Conference Proceed-ings.* San Diego, CA. June 20-22, 2006; 863:193–213.

is conscious, mentally aware perception of future events; presentiment is unconscious, somatically aware perception of them.

Radin's experiments were replicated by HeartMath scientist Rollin McCraty, PhD, and his team, this time looking at presentiment in the heart. Following Radin's protocol, McCraty looked at heart rate variability (HRV) in response to randomly generated calm photos vs. emotional photos. They found that HRV "presponded" an average of 6 seconds before an emotionally charged photo was shown.[10,11]

Somatic pre-sponse is well described in *Alice's Adventures in Wonderland* and *Through the Looking-Glass*. In these classics by Lewis Carroll, the White Queen in the Looking-Glass World lives backward in time. She cries out in pain *before*, rather than *because*, she pricks her thumb on the pin of her brooch. When the painful event happens, she does not react. She has already pre-acted!

Presentiment in Animals

There is a long anecdotal history of animals who pre-sense natural disasters such as earthquakes and tsunamis. Explanations offered for these observations include the animals' sensitivities to geomagnetic, electromagnetic, and atmospheric disruptions prior to such events. Another possibility is that,

10 McCraty R, Atkinson M, Bradley RT. Electrophysiological evidence of intuition: part 1. The surprising role of the heart. *J Altern Complement Med*. 2004; 10(1):133–43.

11 Since HRV is also a proxy for sympathetic nervous system activity, we cannot conclude that the heart itself, any more than a sweat gland, is independently presponding to stimuli. It might be that the presponse in both end-organs, skin and heart, originates in the amygdala.

like humans, animals experience presentiment effects.

Intrigued by mounting evidence for human presentiment, researchers have begun to expand this line of inquiry into animal behavior. A study by Chester Wildey, inspired by Dean Radin's work, exposed earthworms to a randomly generated sequence of mechanical vibrations, simulating an earthquake. Wildey and his worms performed control trials with no vibrations.[12] A second study, by Fernando Alvarez, also informed by Radin's results, consisted of showing to Bengalese finches a randomly generated series of videos with the hated horseshoe whip snake vs. no snake.[13] Both the worms and the birds reacted to the stimuli ahead of time. In particular, Alvarez's results showed that the birds reacted to the snake video clip at least 9 seconds before it was shown.

With horse-rider pairs who are intuitively tuned in to eachother, many horses know what the rider is going to ask several seconds before the request is initiated. This type of presentiment occurs even on a new trail where, unlike in arena work, patterns have not been established and the rider herself might not know what she will need to navigate. Is it possible that some part of the horse's body can anticipate the rider's request before it is even made—possibly even before the rider knows what she is going to ask?

When we do the activities described in part IV, we open ourselves to the possibility that we will experience telepathic communication and presentiment phenomena between ourselves and the horses. Ultimately, it doesn't matter whether

---

12 Wildey C. Impulse Response of Biological Systems. Master's thesis. Department of Electrical Engineering, University of Texas at Arlington. 2001.

13 Alvarez F. Anticipatory alarm behavior in Bengalese finches. *J Sci Explor.* 2010; 24(4):599-610.

we have become super sensitive at reading somatic cues and sensing emotions or whether we have crossed over into telepathy and presentiment. We seek to develop all kinds of empathic awareness that can bring us peace and joy.

Before we get to the practices that develop empathic awareness, we'll look further at the body and embodiment in part II.

Part II

Bodies of Knowledge: Somatics in Philosophy and Physiology

4

I Sing the Body

Original Sin, Original Grace, and Body Image

And if the body were not the soul, what is the soul?
—Walt Whitman, "I Sing the Body Electric," *Leaves of Grass*

"Tell me the truth, does this saddle make me look fat?"

*H*orses don't have hang-ups about body image. They got the memo, for which humans seem to have been out of the loop, about being made in God's image. Horses in pasture eat, run, play, fart, eliminate, and copulate unselfconsciously. They are oblivious to human esthetics in ways not accorded to our domestic pets. A core message of Equine-imity is that mental and emotional stress can be released using the other two functions in the Jungian quaternity: the somatosensory and the intuitive, or spiritual. To do so, we need to allow ourselves unabashed somatic expression. By observing the physical joy of animals and by understanding the origins of the inhibitions we might hold, we are better able to free ourselves to de-stress in whatever body we inhabit.

Religious Views of the Body

Do you not know that your body is a temple of the Holy Spirit within you, whom you have from God?

—1 Corinthians 6:19

The Bible tells us we are made in God's image. Biblical scholars interpret this allusion to mean not the physical image of God, but the image-ination of God's mind and soul. It is probably more correct to say that people create depictions of God, gods, and goddesses—whether a bearded Caucasian male or fierce-faced female dancing demons—in our own image. Nevertheless, the question of the Divine expressed in the body is universal in world religions; in spiritual philosophies such as Daoism and Kabbalah; and in somatic rituals such as Sufi dancing, with its whirling dervishes, and Holy Communion.

So how did humans become prey to body shaming? In the beginning, the Judeo-Christian parable of original sin was body related. God told Adam and Eve they could eat anything they wanted—carbs, trans fats, salt on everything. Only the fruit of a certain tree was forbidden. We refer to it as the Tree of Knowledge; however, its full name was the Tree of Knowledge of Good and Evil. After eating the apple, the knowledge that came to Adam and Eve was like, OMG!—we're naked! Naked and ashamed of the sinfulness of the bare body.

Since the epochs of Genesis and similar creation stories, religions have arrogated to themselves rituals for both sanctifying and vilifying the body. In everything from circumcision to suicide bombing, from fasting to feasting to flagellation to female genital mutilation, the body is asked to enter into a covenant with the Deity or with the Soul. And however untenable it is to generalize about the Christian view of the body or the Islamic view or Buddhist view, each faith preaches a more or less consistent set of beliefs, prescriptions, and proscriptions with regard to bodies.[1]

Philosopher and mystic Jane Roberts taught that we are born into a state of original grace.[2] Our belief in ourselves as sinners is a conditioned response to the human-made convictions that require atonement, often through physical suffering, just for having been born into a body. In *Adam, Eve, and the Serpent*, Elaine Pagels presents a scholarly, profound, and beautifully written history of original sin and its ties with sexuality vs. chastity.[3] According to Pagels, original sin was largely the invention of fifth-century theologians,

1   Lenore Friedman and Susan Moon. *Being Bodies: Buddhist Women on the Paradox of Embodiment* (Boulder, CO: Shambhala, 1997).

2   Jane Roberts. *The Nature of Personal Reality* (New York: Prentice Hall, 1974. Novato, CA: Amber-Allen/New World Library Reprint, 1994).

3   Elaine Pagels. *Adam, Eve, and the Serpent: Sex and Politics in Early Christianity* (New York: Vintage, 1989).

most prominently St. Augustine. Augustine reinterpreted the creation story from one that portrays Adam's free will to one that exposes Adam's sinfulness. This dogma married the church and state of Augustine's time for the expedient of getting in bed — chastely, of course — with the Roman rulers. A populace that could be shamed into an ideology that rendered them sinful from birth could be politically controlled through doctrines of transgression, atonement, and salvation.

Historically, religion dictated how the body was seen and what somatic behaviors were appropriate or required in relation to a deity or to the church. Yoga, now widely taught in classes ranging from the ascetic to the athletic, originated with practices that included the severities of physical renunciation.

The Italian monk and patron saint of animals, St. Francis of Assisi, was a kind and humble soul who preached love and acceptance. Although he was highly compassionate to others, he believed in the doctrine of mortification of the flesh and was brutally cruel to his own body. He referred to his body as "Brother Ass" and subjected it to extremes of fasting and flagellation. Emaciated and suffering from multiple illnesses, St. Francis died at the age of forty-four.

In modern Western society, one's culture, and sometimes one's politics, tend to override religion in dictating somatic values. For example, starting in 2009 and reaching a peak in 2016, the French government banned the burkini, a portmanteau of burka and bikini. The garment is a full-body covering worn by Muslim women who wish to use public beaches while honoring the modesty requirements of Islam. Ongoing controversy around the burkini reflects a complex clash of politics and ideologies. These include state-enforced secularism, Islamophobia, religious bigotry, and feminism, the latter possibly guilty of cultural insensitivity with regard to self-determination for Muslim women.

How was, and is, the body viewed in your family? Did everyone walk around the house nude? Did someone chastise you for playing with your food or with yourself? Who taught you about the birds and bees? Tampons? Shaving? What was the correct number of times per day to brush your teeth? Some families perpetuate cultural, religious, and philosophical traditions that hold the body to be the cause and effect of sin and shame. Other families embrace the body as the seat of guiltless pleasures and as the Soul made physical in God's (or gods' or goddesses') image.

When we learn to consecrate the body as a temple, a place of spiritual refuge and reinvigoration, we reduce the stress caused by a worried mind and by recurrent negative emotions, including those of somatic self-loathing. Adornments of the body with clothes, jewelry, makeup, and tattoos can be gestures of self-blessing.[4] Somato-spiritual practices such as tai ji, qigong, aikido, and yoga also sanctify the body.

For centuries, religious and social conventions dictated that women ride sidesaddle in billowing skirts rather than astride, or cross-saddle, in trousers. Although women of the Tang Dynasty and ranching women of the American West rode astride, in most of Europe and America it was considered unladylike to spread one's thighs apart. Worse, riding astride was believed, even by medical professionals who should have known better, to cause loss of a girl's virginity.[5]

---

4   However, most Conservative, Reform, and Orthodox rabbis interpret the Old Testament as ruling that tattoos are taboo.

5   While it is possible to rupture the hymen during vigorous sports and other activities, "losing virginity" is considered a deliberate psycho-sexual act.

The New Body Religions

Discomfort with one's body is a key driver of what essayist Anne Lamott calls "toxic self-consciousness." Adolf Hitler's Nazi Party of 1930s and '40s Germany fostered the cult of body perfection as part of Aryan supremacy. The trendsetters of high fashion, Hollywood, and elite sports promote specific body types, often drugged, starved, or Photoshopped into a perverse esthetic. Obsession with these norms alienates us from our bodies and drives us to achieve these ideals—often justified as quests for health—with disfiguring surgery, harmful drugs, and X-treme dieting at, ironically, great stress to the body. To some extent the medical profession is the unindicted coconspirator of the movie, sports, and fashion industries. Medical moralism implies that only slim, neurotypical bodies with low cholesterol and sun-blocked skin are healthy and attractive. In Los Angeles, arguably the narcissism capital of the world, local newspapers carry ads for physicians selling

fixes for tummies too fat and lips too thin, for bald heads and hairy legs, for XL thighs and AA breasts.

It was not always this way. Depictions of the human body in prehistoric times exalted fat women. These so-called Venus figurines show female bodies with pendulous breasts, rotund abdomens, and fat thighs. The Venus of Willendorf, found near Willendorf, Austria, was carved between

28,000 and 24,000 BCE. Given its symmetrical distribution of fat, archeologists theorize that the figure is obese rather than pregnant. In those days, fat was highly prized for survival during lean times between successful hunts.

Now, 30,000 years after the Willendorf Venus, many of us, especially women, get body shamed into sucking in our tummies in order to appear thinner. In the nineteenth century, both men and women wore corsets and girdles to achieve svelte shapes. Trussed like a Thanksgiving turkey or compressed into Spanx (which has been compared to sausage casing), we are smooshed into the confined, shallow chest breathing that is both a cause and a symptom of stress. Medical warnings about these shapewear garments describe risks of heartburn and acid reflux, stress incontinence, bladder and yeast infections, and blood clots. As was noted by Cindy LaFavre York in the Los Angeles Times, "Control-top pantyhose can literally squeeze the life out of you."[6]

My body shame victimization came in the form of a thick curly mop and Eastern European thunder thighs at a time when the Joni Mitchell starving folksinger look, with toothpick legs and long straight hair, was in vogue for white girls. If you had come to my house on date night, you would have seen me hunched over an ironing board reeking from the smell of singed hair. It didn't help that I was the only girl among seven male siblings and cousins who all had shiny, straight hair. The boys delighted in taunting me with the hair-shaming epithets "Bubbles" and "Brillo," knowing it would drive me to fight or flight.

The racism-related conked hair of the 1920s to '60s was a

6 Cindy LaFavre Yorks, "Under control: Pantyhose that promise to flatten—and flatter—you are improving. We tested six versions." *Los Angeles Times.* March 18, 1994.

small modification compared with today's re-architecting of our birth bodies. Mutilating the body chemically and surgically in the quest for health, beauty, and gender identity carries financial and psychological costs that deny what it means to be made in a god's image.

In contrast, nonhuman animals are naturally at home in their body sanctuaries. For them, each somatic event is unfiltered by psychological overlay or endless cognitive analysis. When something unpleasant occurs in their bodies, they don't anguish over "Why me? Why this? Why now?" Yea, blessèd are those that dwell in the house of phenomenology, for they know only pure and direct body experience.

On some level we humans yearn for this animal freedom. Perhaps this is one reason we embrace animal bodies in our storytelling. Winnie the Pooh, Aesop's fables, and The Black Stallion encourage children to identify physically and psychologically with animals, a fantasy we abandon as adults. Think back to childhood. What animal did you identify with? In Equine-imity, we play a game with the herd, choosing a horse whose body we would trade places with for a few hours. We ask, Do we want to be the calm horse or the running horse; the lone horse or the horse flanked by buddies? Images of centaurs and tales of shape-shifting from myths like the Frog Prince and the Twilight Saga (I, predictably, was on werewolf Team Jacob) appeal to our desire to experience an altered consciousness inside an animal body. Aboriginal shamans in all cultures, from Siberia to South America, assume animal shapes for healing and ceremonial magic. As I relate in chapter 7, The Shaman on the Shard, qigong is said to have originated from shamans watching animals.

Many people, especially women, vividly remember that when they were young they felt as if they were horses. They didn't pretend to be horses. They physically, emotionally, and mentally were horses. My good friend Sheri, a physician and yoga teacher, relates that during her horse-crazy, horse-body phase around age ten, she would get down on all fours and eat oats from a bowl.

Compared with household dogs and cats, horses are minimally saddled with human moral, esthetic, and hygienic prejudices. In contrast, our pet dogs and cats are asked to adapt to our standards for tidy, tranquil, odor-free homes. They are beholden to our regimens for feeding, working, walking them outdoors, and sleeping. Even before we chastise him, Spot may express shame and guilt by slinking off with his tail between his legs if he has an "accident" or steals a steak off the counter. Horses have no such remorse. They use their bodies as a source of joy and literally as a vehicle to release stress. It is for this reason that horses, on the border between feral and domestic sensibilities, are best suited to teach us to live naturally in our bodies.

Additional Reading

Sarah Coakley, ed. *Religion and the Body* (New York: Cambridge University Press, 2000).

Thomas P. Kasulis, Roger T. Ames, and Wimal Dissanayake, eds. *Self as Body in Asian Theory and Practice* (Albany, New York: SUNY Press, 1993).

John Robb and Oliver J. T. Harris, eds. *The Body in History: Europe from the Paleolithic to the Future* (New York: Cambridge University Press, 2013).

5

JUNGER THAN SPRINGTIME

THE FOUR WAYS OF MIND-BODY WISDOM

Freud had it wrong. You can't fix the mind with the mind.
—David Mamet, playwright[1]

A core message of Equine-imity is that when negative thoughts and emotions create stress, we can call on somatic and spiritual practices to bring us happiness and contentment. Thoughts, emotions, sensations, and instinct are the Four Ways of Wisdom that we are learning in order to balance and integrate for healthy living.

Carl Gustav Jung designated these four modes of functioning as psychological types.[2] Based on Druidic and alchemical traditions before him, Jung named the functions thinking, feeling, sensation, and intuition. For each of us, one of the four is usually dominant—what Jung called the superior function. The superior function dictates two main behaviors: how we discern truth and how we deal with stress. What is your first resort when faced with a crisis? Do you fire up Google to

---

1 Binah: David Mamet with Michael Krasny. *The* New Yorker *Radio Hour*. KALW Public Radio. San Francisco. May 3, 2018.

2 Carl Gustav Jung. *Psychological Types. Collected Works, Volume 6* (Bollingen, 1921).

get information (intellectual)? Do you eat chocolate, go for a two-mile walk, or waste away in Margaritaville (sensory)? Do you call Mom (emotional)? Do you meditate or pray for guidance (intuitive/spiritual)?

In a somewhat warped but energetic display of lay psychology and entrepreneurship, Katharine Cook Briggs, a Carl Jung groupie, and her daughter, Isabel Briggs Myers, popularized psychological type theory. Their neo-Jungian Myers-Briggs Type Indicator (MBTI) is deemed by its licensing company, and may well be, the world's most popular questionnaire for personality type. Its North American version, with ninety-three forced-choice questions, is widely used in business, professional, and party game settings. Whatever its scientific validity, or lack thereof, the MBTI has taught us to embrace the diversity of the Four Ways. Natural horsemanship gurus Pat and Linda Parelli have developed a sort of MBTI for horses. Their Horsenality indicator classifies horses along perpendicular axes of left or right brain and introvert or extrovert. A common theme in testimonials from users of the Horsenality map is gratitude for the understanding that many behavior problems in their horses can be reframed as Horsenality traits.

The intellect is the most highly developed Jungian function in humans and is praised for its supremacy in science and technology. In industrialized nations, validation of experience is often held to a gold standard of logic and rationality. But the demand that all choices be rational or scientific assumes that there can be only one benchmark of intelligence; the implication is that only the intellect can be the arbiter of reality. However, overreliance on the intellect is responsible for much of the dehumanization and alienation of society.

Rationalization of emotions gone awry can lead to an unbending ideology of religious and political extremism. The result is racism, wars, and hate crimes. Rabid rationality must be tempered with the wisdom of compassion and forgiveness.

Although the intellect is often the most highly prized function, each way of knowing contributes to our overall picture of reality and has both normal, or benevolent, and abnormal, or pathological, forms of expression. And while no function is expressed in a pure form, the following table gives a general idea of the balance of the Four Ways of Wisdom.

Modality/ Way of Wisdom	Examples	Positive or Healthy Expression	Negative or Pathological Expression
Intellect	Logic, discrimination, classification, analysis	Scientific discoveries, technology, inventions, investigative journalism	Worry, schizophrenia, mental retardation, senile dementias, white supremacy
Emotion	Love, hate, fear, anger, courage, disappointment, joy	Romance, charity, compassion, sympathy, performing arts	Depression, hate crimes, panic attacks, bipolar disorder, suicide
Sensation	Sight, hearing, taste, smell, touch	Sports, dance, cooking, massage	Somatic pain, hallucinations, eating disorders, tinnitus
Intuition	Hunches, dreams, instincts, religiosity and spirituality, faith	Artistic inspiration, meditation, prayer, telepathy	Paranoia, demonic possession, religious fanaticism

Each modality is a form of intelligence and each has its expression of genius. Marie Curie, San Francisco 49ers wide receiver Jerry Rice, Best Actress Whoopi Goldberg, and His Holiness the Fourteenth Dalai Lama are examples of intellectual, physical, emotive, and spiritual genius respectively. And since no function acts independently, geniuses owe their accomplishments to input from more than one modality. Achievements that appear to be intellectual, such as the invention of the sewing machine and the chemistry of the benzene ring, were first received in dreams, part of the intuitive function. As was noted in our discussion of archetypes in chapter 3, Jung believed that the goal of a lifetime is the individuation process by which we fully develop our psyches. The individuated psyche balances all Four Ways of Wisdom and integrates all the archetypes so they collaboratively inform all beliefs, decisions, and behaviors.

The Mind-Body Problem

Logic is the beginning of wisdom, not the end.
—Mr. Spock, *Star Trek VI: The Undiscovered Country*

Individuation requires that we make our peace with the overarching "mind-body problem." For centuries before and decades after Jung, philosophers, neuroscientists, theologians, and psychologists have addressed the real or imagined separation of mind and body, brain and consciousness, body and soul. The division between the mental and the material, called mind-body dualism, is credited to, or blamed on, French philosopher René Descartes (1596–1650). In long, convoluted treatises on the distinction between the mind and the brain, Descartes started us on our way to the disconnect between science and spirit. In fact, the teaching of Cartesian dualism was banned by the Catholic Church due to hairsplitting over whether and how the Eucharist, the wafer and wine dispensed at Holy Communion, could be literally transformed into the body and blood of Jesus Christ.[3]

In the human world, especially in the West, we often experience mind-body conflict. When the Four Ways of Wisdom are out of harmony, our mental machinations are at odds with our emotions, instincts, and gut senses. The split is most apparent in decision making when we allow logic to veto all other input. Many rationalized choices of school, career, or mate turn out to be disappointing or downright destructive if we ignore the wisdom of feelings and instincts.

The mind-body split is also evident when we develop health problems from having neglected or abused our bodies in deference to intellectual pursuits. During my ten years as the physician at Apple Computer, I saw many brainy, bright new hires arrive thin and fit right out of college only to gain thirty pounds and develop high blood pressure in their first couple of years in the corporation. Fourteen hours a day at the computer and high salaries that afforded fancy cars—no need to ride that old bike anymore!—and big, late-night,

---

3   Descartes also denied that animals had reason, intelligence, or souls. He argued that any sensations and emotions, like pain and anxiety, felt by animals could be explained mechanistically by brain anatomy and chemistry. (See the definition of epiphenomenalism in chapter 3.) Although Descartes' views were not universally accepted, they allowed many Europeans and Americans to commit animal cruelty without guilt. The view that animals were separate from humanity and merely machines sanctioned animal maltreatment. Charles Darwin's publications in the middle of the 1800s tended to humanize animals, or rather, animalize humans, and paved the way for animal rights movements.

liquor-drenched restaurant meals contributed to the loss of their health and fitness.

Illnesses resulting from stress are primarily linked to overwrought thinking and runaway emotions. Our intellectual abilities are engaged so strenuously and so automatically for problem solving that they are always front and center when trouble arises. We try to fight fire with fire. We attempt to use the mind to resolve the problems it created. We worry, berate ourselves, and toss and turn at night with obsessive thoughts. Add the emotional overlay to a worried mind, and we fall into a bubbling cauldron of emotionally charged worries or mentally justified negative emotions.

Mindfulness and Bodyfulness in Horses

My horse Ariel is head down in the new green grass after a February rain. She is totally absorbed in grazing. Not the desultory nibbling of a horse who has been grazing for hours, but the voracious tearing of the long blades, one bunch still hanging from her mouth while she rips out the next clump. If my husband ate that way, I'd want to body shame him with a cluck of my tongue and a roll of my eyes in double-standardization across species. Ariel is completely focused on the grass. She is not going over the mistakes from our last ride or wondering whether leaves on trees are also good to eat. She is not even forming thoughts like, "What excellent grass!" that verbalize what her attention is on. For now, she isn't doing the grazing, she is the grazing. She is the mind-bodyfulness we strive for in our meditation and yoga classes, trying to just be present in our bodies.

Animals don't pit mind against body. Body sensations and emotions are the stuff of their direct experience. They don't think about them; they just feel them, in both senses in which the English language confounds emotional feeling and physical sensing: I feel happy. I feel cold. There isn't even a common word to describe psychospiritual perceptions. We don't say, "I intuit, therefore I am." We use the vague, all-purpose, "I sense that you are sad" or "I have a feeling you're going to like this book."

Horses have highly developed nonintellectual ways of wisdom including, we surmise, a sixth sense that was crucial to their survival. From horses we learn to expand and trust our sensory, emotional, and instinctual awareness and to add these dimensions of knowing to our life paths and decisions. In somatic horsemanship, we emphasize the development of our sensory and spiritual abilities to promote stressless physical health and calm emotions. Horses use their somato-intuitive wisdom when deciding who will be a friend or a mate. But they don't, as far as we know, form cognitive judgments based on instinctual preferences. They don't, for example, say, "That mare's mane falls to the right and mine falls to the left. She must be a jerk."

Eat, Pray, Love, Reflect—Sensing, Intuition, and The Four Ways in Balance

If over-thinking and over-emoting are responsible for most stress responses, from whence cometh our help? The two ways of wisdom that can best act as de-stressors are sensing and intuition. Most of this book is dedicated to the sensing, somatic function. Now we will consider intuition and its higher octave: extrasensory perception.

Intuition has many meanings. It is generally defined as

the ability to acquire knowledge without proof, evidence, or conscious reasoning. It is the direct perception of truths and facts independent of any logical process.

My definition of intuition includes information that comes from sensory cues or from the innate instinctual drives of the organism. For example, you can intuit how a person feels by reading her body language. Highly intuitive people will know if a person is forcing a smile, yet really feels sad or angry despite the big, fake grin. Conversely, a hallmark of persons on the autism spectrum, including intellectually gifted persons with Asperger's, is the inability to read facial expressions or respond appropriately to social cues.

Horses instinctively shy from unfamiliar objects, although their assessment of the danger posed by the object is often in error. That soda can blowing across the ground will not attack them. So instincts, while protective, may lead to fake news.

An extension of intuition that has no apparent sensory source is input that comes from extrasensory ranges of perception. Other names that are applied to this phenomenon are precognition (knowing something ahead of time, as in precognitive dreams), telepathy (mind-to-mind communication), clairaudience (hearing valid information from sounds that are not physically present), and clairsentience or psychometry (receiving information from an object: for example, locating a lost puppy by holding his toy).

In addition to being finely tuned to sensory input, horses often act as if they are processing extrasensory information. Rupert Sheldrake's *Dogs That Know When Their Owners Are Coming Home* includes stories of horses with this sixth sense. Research by Dean Radin, described in chapter 3, suggests that the horse's body, like ours, can "pre-spond" to somatic events that will occur a few seconds later. So when you interact with a horse, you will decide for yourself whether she is reacting (or pre-acting) to your ch'i, to something you've stimulated in one of her five senses, or to a telepathic message you are consciously or unconsciously sending. You will also decide whether you are reacting (or pre-acting) to her ch'i, to her stimulating of one of your five senses, to your projections of your inner self onto her, or to a telepathic message she is sending.

6

WHOA, NELLIE! GO, NELLIE!

Stress and Stress Reduction in Humans and Horses

Behind me a noose stood empty and before me the land was wild. There would be riders behind me now, eager to hang me again, for they were fierce and bitter men with hatred for me.

Suddenly the roan blew loudly, and I could see his head was up and he was listening, watching something.

—Louis L'Amour, *Passin' Through*

L ouis L'Amour's heroes, upon whom many Western movie characters are based, are under constant stress. They are the strong, silent good guys pursued by hired gunslingers, evil cattle barons, and corrupt lawmen. Alone in the searing desert, snowy mountains, and dark forests, good guys and bad guys alike depend on their horses to warn them of any sign of trouble. In the passage above, the horse senses danger and reacts with the typical equine stress response of "blowing"—a sudden snorty sound through widely dilated nostrils.

In Westerns, the ravages of a perilous lifestyle were offset by the cowboy's (and cowgirl's and Indian's) courageous, optimistic attitudes and by the fact that cowpunchers, mountain men, and indigenous peoples lived as one with nature in the outdoors. Neither these humans nor their horses, apparently, suffered from ulcers, colic, heart attacks, or immune dysfunction. Horses and humans had similar responses to acute stress, mainly in the form of the fight-or-flight reaction. (Horses ran; cowboys and Calamity Jane shot it out.)

What follows in this chapter are the biological and psychological concepts of stress that are essential to Equine-imity theory and practice. For a more comprehensive layperson's introduction to stress, read Robert M. Sapolsky's brilliant and humorous *Why Zebras Don't Get Ulcers*.[1]

In Equine-imity we ask, why were cowboys and First Peoples and their horses more like Sapolsky's zebras than like twenty-first-century humans and our domesticated horses?

What Is Stress?

> *It was all bad cards and slow horses.*
>
> —Cowboy's lament after a stressful day

Stress is a fact of life. Every living being, from the first single-celled organism to the largest, most evolved species, has faced illness, injury, predation, and death. Each cell experiences stress individually, according to its nature. The outer cell membrane and the membranes of the cell's internal organelles, such as the nucleus and mitochondria, have receptors for

---

1   Robert M. Sapolsky. *Why Zebras Don't Get Ulcers: An Updated Guide to Stress, Stress Related Diseases, and Coping*, second revised edition (New York: W. H. Freeman, 1998).

stress hormones.[2] Modern humans are subject to short-term stressors like traffic jams and waiting on hold for customer "service," the longer-term stress of work and family demands, and the chronic stress of poor socioeconomic conditions and political persecution.

The word *stress* has come full circle in designating first psychological, then mechanical, then again psychosocial dynamics. Eight hundred years ago, the concept of emotional *distress* came from the Latin *strictus*, meaning compressed, drawn together, or tight. Some of our words to describe stress retain this sense of feeling constricted, pressured, and uptight.

With the introduction of Isaac Newton's laws of classical physics in the seventeenth century, *stress* came to mean a force applied to an inanimate object. *Strain* was the result of mechanical stress as, for example, a measure of the tensile strength of a wire.

In the early twentieth century, physiologists reclaimed the concept of stress and strain to describe the human condition. They used the term *stressor* as something that produces biological stress. The physiological reaction, which in mechanical science is strain, is termed the stress response.

The first scientist to use *stress* in a biomedical rather than an engineering sense was Harvard physiology professor Walter B. Cannon (1871–1945). In 1914, Cannon coined the term, and described the physiology of, the fight-or-flight response as our two main options for dealing with an in-your-face stressor.[3] The fight-or-flight response is characterized by an outpouring of hormones and by subjective feelings of anxiety

2   For an excellent discussion of stress at the cellular level, see *Secrets of Your Cells: Discovering Your Body's Inner Intelligence* by Sondra Barrett, PhD (Boulder, CO: Sounds True, 2013).

3   Cannon WB. The interrelations of emotions as suggested by recent physiological researches. *Am J Psych.* 1914; 25(2):256-282.

or fear—even panic. In predator species such as humans, fight reflexes often predominate. For prey animals like horses, the choice is usually to flee first, ask questions later.

Wire and Haywire

The stress response is not an innate property of our bodies like the tensile strength of a wire. All wires of the same physical makeup and configuration have the same response to an applied force. But humans are not wires. When we go haywire, our behavior is determined by our conditioning, character, moods, diet, sleep quality, social support systems, and other variables. The degree of strain we feel for any applied stressor centers on a factor that psychologists have long had difficulty in defining with objective, quantitative data: the role of personal meaning.

When I was in clinical practice, I was amazed at the composure with which some patients faced a life-or-death procedure like heart surgery, while others had the flight response triggered by the mere sight of a needle. It's not the event itself that causes our reaction; it's our subjective interpretation of the event and the significance we assign to it.

How we react to short- and long-term stressors is more within our control than we might imagine. Healthy responses to stress can be learned and conditioned. Thoughts that create stress can be replaced with stress-reducing thoughts. This substitution is facilitated when the mind is redirected to pleasurable activities, especially those involving the whole body.

We will see throughout this book how we can override our conditioned responses to stress by deliberately choosing different activities and patterns of behavior.

How Does Stress Affect Our Health?

In the heat of a stressful event, some systems are go, go, go. Pathways that start in the brain and go down to the adrenal glands result in the release of two main stress hormones: adrenalin, for immediate (within seconds) response, and cortisol, the slightly (by a few minutes) delayed response. Adrenalin speeds up the heart for the delivery of more oxygenated blood to the fighting or fleeing muscles. Cortisol increases blood glucose to provide more fuel.

Other systems are stop, stop, stop. The stress response slows digestion and, longer term, can cause women to stop ovulating and menstruating. These adaptations are the body's acknowledgment that times of stress are not good for relaxing at a seven-course meal or for bringing new members of the species into the world.

These responses, like much of our anatomy and physiology, are left over from our early evolution. For example, in our cave days, our hairy bodies kept us warm; now, thousands of years later, we have waxing salons. The extremes of the stress response, which Hans Selye called the General Adaptation Syndrome, are chief among those outdated functions. They prepare the body for an all-out war on danger.

The problem is that the General Adaptation Syndrome is too general. It does not discriminate between ancient stressors and modern stressors. So the adrenal storm causes your blood pressure to shoot up to 190 whether you are running from a saber-toothed tiger or arguing with your teenager. Some researchers have observed that even notifications from smartphones increase blood cortisol levels.

Sapolsky writes:

This is the critical point of this book: if you are a zebra running for your life, or a lion sprinting for your meal, your body's physiological response mechanisms are superbly adapted for dealing with such short-term physical emergencies. For the vast majority of beasts on this planet, stress is about a short-term crisis, after which either it's over with or you're over with. When we sit around and worry about stressful things, we turn on the same physiological responses—but they are potentially a disaster when provoked chronically. A large body of evidence suggests that stress-related disease emerges, predominantly, out of the fact that we so often activate a physiological system that has evolved for responding to acute physical emergencies, but we turn it on for months on end, worrying about mortgages, relationships, and promotions.[4]

So even when a stressor is purely psychological, such as during a heated argument, the adrenals behave as if life and death are at stake. They get this message from the hypothalamus, the brain's link between the nervous system and the endocrine system. The hypothalamus responds to the thought of clear and present danger and the thought of vague and future danger in the same mindless way.

Acute (short-term, in-the-moment) stress can cause indigestion, headaches, a racing heart, skin rashes, and susceptibility to colds. With chronic (long-term, ongoing) stress, these conditions become more severe and persist in the form of gastric ulcers, inflammatory bowel disease, heart attacks, muscle wasting, and more serious (than a cold) immune

---

4   Sapolsky, *Why Zebras Don't Get Ulcers*, 30.

dysfunction. Even susceptibility to some cancers has been shown to have a stress component resulting from the suppression of immune cells that destroy mutations. Due to the organ damage that may result from long-term secretion of adrenalin and cortisol, they are known as the "wear and tear" hormones.

One way to understand the difference between acute and chronic stress is to compare *fear* and *worry.* Fear is an emotion. It arises in response to something in the now—a pop quiz, an icy road, flames leaping from the stove. Worry is a mental construct. It is the *thought* of something that could produce fear in the future. Worrying can produce strong emotions about something that might or might not happen: your three-year-old might not get into Harvard, climate change might make the ocean flood your city, you might catch covid on your flight to Chicago. The adrenals don't know the difference between emotions caused by an actual threat (fear) and emotions caused by a possible threat (worry). That's why it's important to master the horse's technique of going back to grazing, deliberately choosing not to worry over imagined scenarios, and releasing fear when the fire is out.

It's important to note that chemical substances like adrenalin don't in themselves make us feel stressed. The adrenalin rush of skydiving feels different from the adrenalin outpouring of an event we didn't volunteer for. The feeling of stress is a mental, psychological overlay on the chemical, hormonal effect.

The Mind-Brain-Body Connection

Stressful emotions usually start from the thinking part of the brain, the cerebral cortex. Even before any thoughts can form, the body may be aware of raw sensations—the sight of a car about to hit us, the sound of someone screaming, the smell of smoke, the tremor of an earthquake. Sensations create conscious thoughts. Thoughts provoke emotions. Downstream in the brain from the cortex, the tiny amygdala and the hypothalamus are the middlemen between the thinking brain, the emotional brain, and the stress response organs such as the adrenals, stomach, liver, skin, pancreas, blood vessels, and sweat glands.

Strangely, the amygdala can also become activated by stimuli that are not yet conscious. That is, there seems to be direct communication between the sense organs and the amygdala, with cognition of the event literally an afterthought.

More strangely, neuroscientists have not identified the exact spot where, or the process by which, a *thought* produces a *physical response*. They know the location, chemistry, and electrical circuitry of the nervous system. Using microelectrodes, they have looked inside brain cells. They have probed into even tinier brain cell structures such as microtubules and RNA strands. But where is the *thought* itself? Where does it plug into the wiring that runs the rest of the body? Where does the thought of tomorrow's job interview jump the mind-body gap to release stress hormones? Where does the decision to run from a fire become the act of running? The mind-brain-thought-action sequence is one of the great mysteries of psychosomatic medicine.

There is not a unique, one-to-one relationship between thoughts and their biochemical reactions. Different thoughts trigger the same chemicals. Whether your thought is "Oh, what a beautiful symphony" or "Damn! My car won't start," the nerve pathways produce the same adrenalin, cortisol, endorphins, and other substances. In either case, the pathway for this cascade is the autonomic nervous system (ANS). The ANS controls involuntary, often unconscious functions such as blood pressure, heartbeat, digestion, and breathing while asleep. It has two main components: the pants-on-fire sympathetic nervous system and the stop-and-smell-the-roses parasympathetic nervous system. The sympathetic nervous system is the yang, active, propulsive side of the ANS that fires in the fight-or-flight response. The parasympathetic nervous system (PNS), activated by the paired vagus ("vay-gus") nerves, is the restful, yin, receptive side of the ANS that is engaged during back-to-grazing behaviors. The PNS can both calm the body during and after a stressful event and preempt stress by creating a relaxed, peaceful state ahead of a stressor. Activation of the parasympathetic nervous system has been called the "feed and breed," "rest and digest" response or pre-sponse.

The PNS can be deliberately activated by relaxation and meditation activities like qigong, tai ji, and mindfulness-based stress reduction. A remarkable study by Michael Chin and Stefanos Kales compared four groups of subjects in their ability to promote parasympathetic activity.[5] The groups were assigned to perform either meditative breathing, limb movement, a combination of the two, or neither (control group) during the introduction of a mental stressor. Using heart rate variability as an indicator of PNS activity, Chin and Kales found that breathing synchronized with muscle movement leads to significantly more activation of the PNS than either muscle motion or breathing alone. Their results

5   Chin MS and Kales SN. Understanding mind–body disciplines: A pilot study of paced breathing and dynamic muscle contraction on autonomic nervous system reactivity. *Stress Health*. 2019; 35(4):542-548.

suggest that activities like qigong and tai ji might be more optimal for stress reduction than sports-type exercises or sitting meditation.

A third arm of the ANS is the enteric nervous system (ENS) located in the digestive tract. The ENS has been called the "second brain," as it can function without input from the conscious or unconscious brain-mind. Many times our gut feelings, butterflies in the stomach, and inability to stomach something are more trustworthy guides to reality than faulty rationalizations from the cerebral cortex.

Stress and Dreams

When stress is intentionally swept under the rug or subconsciously held inside, the bodymind will try to get our attention. The first line of communication is often nighttime dreams.

In 2004, I was certified as a dream counselor by the Marin Institute for Projective Dreamwork. MIPD's founder and my mentor, the late Jeremy Taylor, held that every dream contains an image that represents our health. Houses, tools, vehicles, and other machines in dreams often symbolize the body and its parts.

As the physician at Apple Computer in California's Silicon Valley, I had a thirty-something patient I'll call Rhonda whose engineering team had undergone a series of cutbacks and layoffs. Rhonda had irritable bowel symptoms that had eluded exact diagnosis and treatment by her GI specialists. One night, Rhonda dreamed that her boss put her teddy bear into an old-fashioned hand-cranked tubular meat grinder. The little stuffed animal was coming out as a liquid. The dream sequence was a yucky but accurate representation of Rhonda's medical condition. Rhonda identified with her beloved child-hood toy and recognized that the meat grinder symbolized her colon. After having this dream, she was finally convinced of the connection between her intestinal problems and stress at work, where the boss was indeed putting everyone through the mill.

If we take to heart Dr. Taylor's adage that life is a waking dream, we can learn to heed the dreamlike scenarios our bodies enact. For instance, aches and pains can be experienced in a symbolic dimension, as if we were having a dream about the affected body parts. Awareness is the key. The Equine-imity opening meditations in chapter 10 enhance somatic awareness through the simple act of tuning in to external and internal stimuli. Body sensations and their symbolic waking-dream-like interpretations, approached with an open, playful mind, can provide the incentive and direction needed to reduce stress. [6]

Distress and Eustress

Not all stress is harmful. Eu ("yoo," as in "euphoria") is a prefix meaning "good." Eustress is good stress. Substitute the word "arousal" for stress and you will get the upside of being revved up.

The Hebbian-Yerkes-Dodson optimal performance curve (next page) illustrates how both too little arousal (boredom) and too much arousal (anxiety) can be harmful to our health. The graph follows a path from a state of low arousal, through a phase of increasing stimulation, to a peak state of eustress

---

6   For a guide to working with the body as a dream, see Kane, B. *Symptom & Significance* at http://www.horsensei.com/publica-tions/SandS/SandS.pdf.

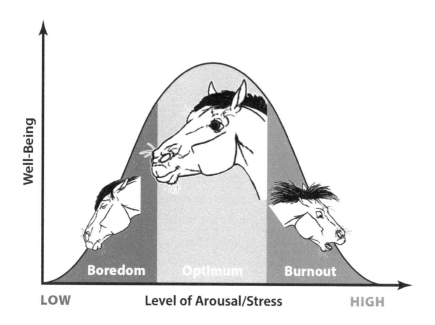

in which we feel most positive, optimistic, and functional. To the right of the optimal zone is the hyperarousal state where we experience the discomfort of too much stress. If the hyperaroused state becomes chronic, as with ongoing aggravation at work, at home, or in society, burnout and illness may result.

The learning challenges and rewards of the Equine-imity 4-Phase Program are designed to keep us in the zone of optimum arousal.

Measuring Stress: Life Events, Daily Hassles, Daily Uplifts

Beginning in the middle of the twentieth century, researchers attempted to quantify the impact of stressful events and predict the degree to which these events can lead to illness. The Holmes-Rahe ("ray-hee") Social Readjustment Scale, also called the Life Change Scale, is the classic example.[7] In 1967, Thomas Holmes and Richard Rahe at the University of Washington asked 374 adults in the Seattle area to rate forty-three life events with regard to how stressful they felt. As a starting point, the researchers arbitrarily assigned to getting married a value of 500 points.

The events included both those felt to be unpleasant, like the death of a loved one, and subjectively happy events that, nonetheless, represented a change from daily routine—marriage, vacations, a job promotion, a new baby. Holmes and Rahe showed that after racking up a certain number of points, we are at risk for getting sick. And it's not just the degree of *negativity* we attach to an event, but the *magnitude* (mathematical absolute value) *of change* for better or worse that contributes to the total number of points. In that sense, our bodies do not distinguish between distress and eustress. Both types of change release adrenalin and cortisol in response to change.

In the 1970s and '80s, researchers refined the work of Holmes and Rahe by creating the Daily Hassles and Uplifts Scale.[8] Their studies measured the stress of daily annoyances such as traffic jams and misplacing one's watch. (Presumably the latter translates to the more ubiquitous and recently acquired hassle of losing one's cell phone.) The researchers concluded that the numerical scores of daily hassles more accurately predict eventual illness than do the scores of major life events. In fact, they reasoned, major life events are stressful *because* they result in more daily hassles. That is, the death of a spouse scores highest on the Holmes-Rahe scale because the

7   Holmes TH and Rahe RH. The social readjustment rating scale. *J Psychosom Res.* 1967;11(2):213-218.

8   Kanner AD et al. Comparison of two modes of stress measurement: daily hassles and uplifts versus major life events. *J Behav Med.* 1981; 4 (1):1-39.

loss of a loved one who can cook, clean, mow the lawn, fix the sink, and offer companionship results in the daily hassles of having to do these things for oneself or do without. These same researchers also quantified the value of *daily uplifts,* like smelling flowers or getting a massage, to offset the toll of daily hassles. Studies of stress reduction interventions such as qigong and tai ji show that these activities act as daily uplifts that help wipe out our hassle points.

Stress in Horses

Saturday, 16 November, 2019. 7:20 a.m. I shuffle into the bathroom and am startled fully awake by the cold tiles under my bare feet. The first chill of autumn has set in. Downstairs in my study, warming my hands around a cup of tea, I open the e-mail sent to our Saturday morning quadrille team. Subject: "Sad News." Rosie, a 23-year-old mare on the team, colicked last night with excruciating pain and had to be guided over the Rainbow Bridge.

Colic, which is pain and usually blockage in the intestines, is the number one cause of death in horses. It most commonly occurs in autumn and spring and when the horse is under stress. Although there is no Holmes-Rahe scale for horses, we know that horses thrive in an unchanging environment. Any variation in their routine or surroundings—the change of seasons, trailering to competitions, alterations in diet, feeding schedule, bedding, stall, or herd composition—can cause colic and other stress illnesses. Horses kept in stalls with set feeding times and little contact with other horses are at higher risk. Horses kept in pastures, where they can graze and socialize 'round the clock, have a lower incidence of colic.

Rosie was an elderly horse who had recently changed

owners. The new owner wanted an older, safer horse to ride. She moved Rosie from her herd in a pasture at a small, quiet farm to a paddock along the main road through our large ranch. Relocating to a world of clanging trucks, squeaking horse trailers, rumbling tractors, and the constant traffic of cars, buses, people, and horses was like moving from a country cottage to midtown Manhattan. Rosie's risk factors for colic were her age, the onset of autumn, and the change of environment—new person, new noisy home, new feed, goodbye old horse buddies.

Our domesticated equines are somewhere between zebras and humans in their responses to stress. Unlike zebras in the wild, our horses and mules are rarely victims of predators such as wolves and lions. However, horses kept in barns exhibit many stall vices such as pacing, weaving, and cribbing. Pacing is walking compulsively back and forth in a cramped space. Weaving means swaying the head and neck from side to side, similar to the repetitive movements of autistic stimming. Cribbing, often accompanied by wind sucking, is chewing on non-food objects like the stall door. In wind sucking, the horse braces his teeth against an immobile object like a fence, then sucks in and swallows air. Wind sucking creates a release of opiate-like endorphins, but also results in a higher risk of colic.

All of these behaviors can be signs of stress or, more likely, boredom. In the latter case, horses housed alone in small, human-convenient enclosures can be far to the left on the Yerkes-Dodson graph. At the far right of the graph are high-performance horses who compete in the upper levels of sports such as dressage, eventing, and endurance. These horses, unlike Sapolsky's zebras, are prone to ulcers. Pastured horses who do not engage in demanding sports rarely get ulcers, rarely colic, and rarely exhibit stall vices unless learned from previously confined horses who come into pasture displaying these behaviors. (Mirror neurons might be active here.)

Horses retain physical and emotional stress from human abuse, poor-fitting tack, and excessive training, performance, and competition demands. Chronic stress from these sources can manifest as sour or depressed moods, illnesses, or lameness. Behavioral changes such as kicking, biting, spooking, and unwillingness to partner in activities might be the horse's cry for help with stress.

In the field of equine-guided learning and therapy (EGLT), there is debate on whether and how much these activities stress the horses who are employed in them. Although on the surface this work doesn't appear very demanding, EGLT practitioners question the extent to which the equines, commonly including mini-horses, might be taking on the emotional burdens of the patients and clients. Thus far, high-quality research has shown no increase in cortisol or other stress indicators in therapy horses.[9,10]

In our first encounters with horses in Equine-imity classes, we spend several minutes simply observing herd dynamics. Usually we notice subtle dominance and submission behaviors. We ask, "Which do you think is the more stressful position for a horse—the bottom of the pecking order or the top?" (What would you guess?) Many people reason that the lower echelons, where the horse gets picked on, is more

9   Malinowski K et al. The effects of equine assisted therapy on plasma cortisol and oxytocin concentrations and heart rate variability in horses and measures of symptoms of post-traumatic stress disorder in veterans. *J Equine Vet Sci.* 2018; 64:17–26.

10   Johnson RA et al. Horses working in therapeutic riding programs: cortisol, adrenocorticotropic hormone, glucose, and behavior stress indicators. *J Equine Vet Sci.* 2017; 57:77-85.

stressful. However, the reverse is true. The horse is a herd animal, comfortable with a consistent place in an ordered society. His goals and expectations for himself are not like ours. He doesn't have to explain to Mom why he's not leadership material. No horse in pasture gets an ulcer because he's not the boss. Once he understands the chain of command, that's okay with him, regardless of his place in line. He's comfortable knowing there's a strong leader and receiving direction from those above him. He is most at ease following a familiar routine of etiquette, obedience, and safety. When it comes to ego pride, he doesn't have a horse in that race. If a dominant horse becomes impaired and can no longer lead, or a new horse on the block shakes up the order of things, that inconsistency translates to stress for the rest of the herd.[11]

The physiology of the General Adaptation Syndrome in horses is nearly identical to that in humans. A horse has an amygdala, with pathways descending to the hypothalamus, down to the pituitary gland, and on down to the adrenal glands. The horse's number one target organ for stress is the intestines, part of the enteric nervous system, where colic occurs. Because horses have less cognitive stress than we do—no mortgages, SATs, or exes unfriending them on Facebook—the ENS might be both the source for and target of stress. Rather than acting as a second brain, the ENS may act more like a primary brain. Horses with chronic stress are also more susceptible to infection and respiratory diseases and can be slower to recover from injuries. Like humans, horses show individualized responses to stress, even within breed lines that are stereotyped as temperamentally "hot" (Arabians and Thoroughbreds), "warm" (Friesians and Hanoverians),

11 Pieper D. The language of horsemanship—how to speak "horse." *Western Horseman.* October 2013.

and "cool" (Budweiser Clydesdales and the American Quarter Horse). Hot horses tend to be spookier, rearing up or bolting when they are afraid. Spooks put the rider in danger of serious injury. No one wants to ride a perilously spooky horse! After a spook, some horses get increasingly amped up. They have a lowered threshold for additional spooking, even from minor sights and sounds. Other horses reestablish their baseline calm by literally or figuratively going back to grazing. These are the horses we wish to emulate.

The two horses I have been closest to, an Arabian and a Quarter Horse, have had very different horsenalities under stress.

In the winter of 2009, I flew to Boise to look at a horse who would be my 100-mile endurance horse.

"Why Boise?" my husband asked. "Aren't there horses in California?"

Well, yes … but. I wanted a horse like Jesse, my endurance rider friend's sweet, calm gray Arabian who had come from that same Idaho ranch. At the beginning of December, the ranch owners, Tom and Carla, told me they had just found another possible Jesse.

So shortly after Christmas, I flew out there to meet this new horse. From the plane window, in the rainy-snowy sky, I saw my first and last circular rainbow. A good omen, I thought.

The ranch was flat and bleak and dotted with sagebrush. On a 10-degree day, I met Cody and rode him over steep, icy mountain trails, where he was surefooted and confident. Idaho is a free-range, fence-out state. Cattle roam freely, and it is incumbent upon landowners to fence them out if they want to protect their property. Cody trotted bravely through the sage, among the cows.

Despite Tom's disclosure that he had come off Cody when

he spooked at a pack of dogs running at him—an understandable reaction in any horse—and despite the fact that Cody was a little jumpy when being led, he was personable and well-mannered and had the sweetest face. He also vetted as a 100-mile endurance prospect, which was what I was after. So after some delays due to snowstorms and impassable roads out of Boise, Cody arrived at Webb Ranch just as the mustard bloomed on the hills.

Over the next two years, Cody proved to be way too reactive for me. At the slightest perturbation, and without warning, he would perform the Arab teleport. In this classic maneuver, the horse lurches sideways off all four legs. He goes horizontally, the rider goes vertically—down. On one occasion, we were riding past a field of shoulder-high wild radish. Suddenly a little foal's head popped up from the purple and white flowers. Cody did the Arab teleport and off I went.

For months after my third unscheduled dismount, my right butt cheek was bruised in the shape of a Nokia 5450. Ultimately, I did not have the seat, skills, or bone density to cope with these repeated antics. More than one professional trainer who worked with him cautioned that Cody might never mature into a completely safe and sage horse.

The most dismaying thing about Cody was that once he got amped up, his spook threshold got lower until something relatively small triggered him to go haywire. This was a horse who did not go back to grazing.

My current horse, Serena, named to encourage a peaceful quality, is a registered American Paint Quarter Horse, a breed known for their calmer dispositions.

Serena's original name was Talula, undoubtedly for Tallulah Bankhead, a movie drama queen of the 1940s. Like her tempestuous Hollywood namesake, Talula was prone to emotional displays, especially in transitions to faster gaits. (We suspect that she was trained and possibly "cowboyed on" by a perfectionist who overcorrected her and punished her for being "wrong.") At times I would accuse her of being an Arabian in a Quarter Horse body. However, although she can be temperamental, she is not spooky. It has taken us three years to synchronize our minds and bodies and to negotiate quiet transitions. Finally we have ceased to jackrabbit into the upper gaits as if we were after the James gang. We have given eachother amazing lessons in blending energy centers in the way of aikido or tai ji Push Hands.

With Cody I lost a lot of trust and self-confidence. My body developed some bad postures and reflexes from riding defensively. Only slowly have I deconditioned those habits by learning to trust Serena. Very little bothers her. And if something does startle her, she makes a little crow hop and then goes back to her baseline equanimity. More importantly, I have learned that Serena's high energy is not her being naughty and disrespectful, as some horse trainers would have us believe.

Horses and humans feed eachother's anxiety. A nervous horse requires a calm rider. A nervous rider can gain confidence from a staid old lesson master.

In addition to the role of influences from her environment, the horse's temperament is partly inherited. Various ancestry lines within a breed are known to be gentle or high strung or grumpy or cooperative. Cody's great-great-great grandsire, Raffles, was a flighty and difficult horse. Serena's great-great-great-great grandsire, Three Bars, was a Thoroughbred known, uncharacteristic of his breed, for an easygoing disposition. His composure was one of the reasons he succeeded in siring offspring who became legends in the American Quarter Horse Hall of Fame.

A fascinating study at a young women's riding academy in Belgium looked at salivary cortisol as a measure of stress in both riders and their horses before, during, and after a show-jumping competition.[12] The results showed that cortisol levels in the girls rose many times from their baseline, while the cortisol levels in the horses rose relatively little. The human cortisol elevations were directly related to the number of show penalties, while horse cortisol levels were inversely related to the number of penalties. That is, horses with bigger cortisol responses were performing better, and the young women with higher cortisols (indicating higher stress) performed more poorly.[13]

Stress Reduction for Humans and Horses

Happily, the elimination of stress has been proven to alleviate and prevent physical and mental illness. Following the 1975 publication of Harvard physician Herbert Benson's classic *The Relaxation Response,*[14] which examined Transcendental Meditation, medical studies have established the stress-reduction and disease-prevention capabilities of several forms of exercise, relaxation, and meditations like qigong and tai ji.

Thousands of years before Dr. Benson, Chinese qigong practitioners choreographed forms for each organ system

---

12 Peeters M et al. Rider and horse salivary cortisol levels during competition and impact on performance. *J Equine Vet Sci.* 2012; 33 (2013):155-160.

13 This study also found that the cortisol level of each horse and rider pair did not correlate.

14 Herbert Benson with Miriam Z. Klipper. *The Relaxation Response.* Expanded edition (New York: Harper, 2000).

and its associated emotion. In modern research conducted in Beijing and other medical centers, the Ba Duan Jin–derived set that we use in Equine-imity has been shown to have significant benefits in reducing stress, promoting sleep, and improving the life satisfaction scores reported by cancer patients.

The movements in the Ba Duan Jin specifically address the organs and emotions that produce the stress hormones. In Equine-imity, we use a five-form subset of the Ba Duan Jin that can be performed on horseback, described in chapter 11. The chapter has a table that shows each form with its related organ system, the negative emotion that gets released through the form during exhalation, and the positive emotion that replaces it during inhalation in the form's final gesture.

Equine-imity as a Multi-Component Stress Reduction Intervention

A major component of qigong, and therefore of Equine-imity, is mindfulness, defined as moment-to-moment, nonjudgmental awareness. Mindfulness training, like the Kabat-Zinn Mindfulness-Based Stress Reduction (MBSR) program, was initially developed for people with chronic pain. Extensive experimental results show that mindfulness-based cognitive and behavioral therapies help relieve a variety of conditions, such as multiple sclerosis, post-traumatic stress, anxiety, substance abuse, suicidal behavior, and eating disorders. In a clever study that sought to isolate the underlying mechanisms of mindfulness training, researchers found that *acceptance* training plus monitoring (awareness) training with a smartphone app reduced stress more than awareness training alone.[15] Acceptance of a situation is an attitude adjustment that can be trained and then willed in times of stress.

Qigong, the core practice in Equine-imity, has been shown to reduce the cortisol response to a stressful task.[16] Equine-assisted psychotherapy also shows clinical promise as a treatment for stress, especially in post-traumatic stress, for which office-based talk therapy has almost literally hit a wall.[17] Related research attests to the value of pet therapies and nature-based therapies. Equine-imity combines elements of qigong, mindfulness, equine-assisted psychotherapy, pet therapy, and nature-based therapy.

Horses, especially those who live in pasture, can avail themselves of several techniques for stress relief. Peaceful grazing, exuberant rolling on the ground, and rubbing on trees are spa treatments for a horse. For horses confined in stalls, high-performance horses, and horses experiencing life transitions, many forms of equine bodywork such as massage, acupuncture, and chiropractic are available. Even the simple ministrations of grooming and bathing by humans offer needed relaxation. Two of the most effective bodywork systems for releasing stress in horses, especially stress accu-

---

15 Linsey EK et al. Acceptance lowers stress reactivity: Dismantling mindfulness training in a randomized controlled trial. *Psychoneuroendocrinology.* 2018; 87:63-73.

16 Ponzio E et al. Qi-gong training reduces basal and stress-elicited cortisol secretion in healthy older adults. *European Journal of Integrative Medicine.* 2015; 73:194-201.

17 For the latest reference to many studies, see the EAGALA (Equine-Assisted Growth and Learning Association) list at https://tinyurl.com/vwx8fs4 and search the National Library of Medicine database for "equine-assisted psychotherapy" at https://www.ncbi.nlm.nih.gov/pubmed.

mulated over many years, are the Masterson Method and Tellington Touch. Your options for a continuing relationship with horses after Equine-imity activities include becoming trained in Masterson or TTouch, for personal pleasure or as a professional path.

Part III

Principles and Practices

7

THE SHAMAN ON THE SHARD

Introduction to Medical Qigong

Most people believe that physicists are explaining the world. Some physicists even believe that, but the Wu Li Masters know that they are only dancing with it.

—Gary Zukav, *The Dancing Wu Li Masters*

The Jedi master in *Star Wars*, Obi-wan Kenobi, had two teachers: Yoda and Qui-Gon Jinn, a name meaning Qi Gong Genie.

Qigong ("chee goong") is an ancient practice consisting of mindful, ballet-like movements coordinated with the dan tien breathing described in chapter 10. Several styles of qigong derive from Daoism, Confucianism, Buddhism, and from later, even twenty-first-century, traditions. Like the philosophies themselves, each style of qigong varies in intent and emphasis, from martial to medical to meditative to the quest for immortality. The purpose of medical qigong, and a side effect of all styles, is to improve health, prevent and cure disease, foster happy aging, and promote longevity. In its most transcendental form as a spiritual practice, qigong promotes the integration of the human body with the Divine Presence.

Archeological evidence supports claims that the origins of qigong lie in ancient shamanic stances depicted here in the pottery of the Yangshao and MaJiaYao cultures of Northern China (5000–3000 BCE). The late archeologist and Harvard professor Kwang-chih Chang saw in the figure a hermaphroditic *wu master*, or priest-shaman. Later observers interpreted the figure to be in a posture of qigong, with ch'i gulping evidenced by the gaping mouth.

Wu shamans of the Han Dynasty (200 BCE–200 CE) performed healing dances they learned from watching animals. An aspect of shamanism common to all cultures is the healer's ability to enter a trance state and assume the form of an animal, known as *shape-shifting*, and communicate with animal spirit guides.

Han Dynasty physician Hua Tuo (145–207 CE), who is known as the Father of Traditional Chinese Medicine

Hua Tuo

(TCM),was the original integrative medicine practitioner. Not only was he the first surgeon to use general anesthesia, with a concoction of wine and opium, but he also continued the shamanic tradition of animal transformations. He based his qigong-like dances on witnessing the self-healing abilities of five animals: tiger, deer, bear, monkey, and crane. Han Tuo used theories of ch'i circulation to explain the functions of the human body, correlating the movements of these five animals with the five major organ systems in all species. His Five Animals Frolics has remained a classic form of medical qigong for more than 1,800 years.

Medical qigong is used to treat, adjunctively or by itself, heart disease, diabetes, arthritis, pain, and mental illness. Both the Five Animals Frolics and Guo Lin New Qigong have been proven especially effective in cancer therapy at Beijing Miyun Capital Tumor Hospital, Beijing University of Chinese Medicine, and other medical centers in China and the United States. Clinical studies show that cancer patients who practice qigong for two to eight hours per day have increased appetite, less depression, decreased pain, higher remission rates, and longer survival when qigong is used alone or integrated with radiation and chemotherapy. In 2005, the National Center for Complementary and Alternative Medicine, one of twenty-seven agencies that made up the National Institutes of Health, acknowledged qigong as a modality of energy medicine, further described in chapter 8, The Ch'i Also Rises.

Qigong in Practice

To stand straight is to give up the burden of insecurity.
To breathe slowly is to take life as it comes,
without allowing memory or expectation to interfere.
Practice qigong to learn that you are part of Nature.
When you breathe, it is the wisdom of nature that breathes you!
—Qigong Master Ken Cohen

Qigong is a standing, sitting, or lying-down dance with slow, graceful, no-impact, no-contortion movements, suitable for people of all ages and physical abilities. It unifies the body, mind, emotions, and spirit in a series of flowing forms coordinated with deep, relaxed breathing.

Many people report that they are unable to achieve a state of relaxation using meditation techniques that require sitting still and clearing the mind. Although sitting methods have millions of adherents, including me on a good day, for many Westerners, catatonic tranquility is neither desirable nor attainable. It is hard to achieve, harder to sustain, and nearly impossible to summon during times of stress.

The appeal of a moving meditation such as qigong lies in the fact that practitioners learn to *direct* energy rather than contain or suppress it. Redirecting energy is a technique used with unruly horses. When it's hard for a horse to maintain his composure, the kindest solution is to ask him to take that energy outside. We can't hold him back, so we ask him to keep moving, sometimes just at the end of our lead rope.

Qigong movements clear the mind of worry while giving it something else to do. Many people who have been unable to stay present in mindfulness classes are capable of unwavering focus when doing qigong or when doing activities with horses—and especially when doing both together. It can be an additional challenge to meditate in indoor spaces like the office buildings where people are getting stressed out in the first place. The mind naturally wanders back to work. Freeing the mind is easier where an outdoor setting with horses provides a change of environment.

Qigong is one of many of Asian-derived movement practices that run the gamut of exertion and intensity. These disciplines range from the more aggressive martial forms such as karate, tae kwon do, kung fu, and aikido to the semi-martial, more meditative art of tai ji, to yoga styles that are themselves on a continuum from spiritual to athletic. All these practices share a trinity of goals for the cultivation and purification of ch'i: personal power, health and longevity, and spiritual development.

Qigong is one of the gentlest ways to move and balance ch'i. *Gong* means work, achievement, or result. So qigong is "energy work," yielding a quantity and quality of ch'i that results from harmonizing breath, body movements, and emotions. I choose qigong, along with tai ji, as my personal practice and as the core practice of Equine-imity because it is simple to learn, easy to perform, and kind on the bodies of humans and horses. Mainly I choose it because with qigong, I have experienced relief of hip pain, a more mellow disposition, better balance, decreased stress responses, and sounder sleep.

Qigong exercises move ch'i so it releases from where it is blocked, fills where it is depleted, and ebbs from where it is in excess. Circulating one's ch'i relies on learning to balance yin and yang by inhaling and exhaling, by cultivating both serenity and vigor, and by extending and withdrawing limbs. Qigong master Zhongxian Wu teaches that any posture, movement, or activity done with conscious attention to the flow of ch'i can be called qigong. [1] When done mindfully, eating, drawing, crafting, dancing, listening to music, washing dishes, and grooming a horse are all forms of qigong.

Chinese language sources estimate there are up to 4,000 different qigong forms from various lineages. That number is growing as modern teachers invent new forms. Equine-imity

1   Zhongxian Wu. *Chinese Shamanic Cosmic Orbit Qigong* (Singing Dragon, 2011).

uses one of the best known and simplest forms of medical qigong, first mentioned in the introduction, the Ba Duan Jin (literally, "eight sections of brocade"; poetically, "eight silken movements"). We have adapted a Shaolin style Ba Duan Jin that adheres closely to the classic forms illustrated in chapter 11. Five of the original eight forms can be performed on horseback. So we call them the *Wu* (five) *Duan Jin*. You will learn them as standing forms in chapter 10 and as forms for horseback in chapter 17. You will learn to do qigong first with your own ch'i and then with the combination of your and the horse's ch'i.

The beginning qigong moves taught in chapter 10 also prepare us for blending our dan tien energy with that of horses in the dan tien press and the dan tien hug during meet and greet in chapter 13. On the ground or on the horse, mindful contact between the two bodies allows an anxiety-quickened human heart, racing at 90 to 120 beats per minute, to slow down in entrainment with the horse's heart, with its resting rate of 40 beats per minute.

Next let's take a closer look at ch'i.

8

The Ch'i Also Rises

The Bioenergetics of Qigong

On a day glowing with October's bright blue weather, four young monks from Shaolin Temple USA arrive at my "office," the 230-acre historic Webb Ranch. Dressed in civvies for the first time in the year I'd known them, they have come to do energy sensing with the horses.[1] These holy men, who are kung fu masters with rock star status in the martial arts world, are heirs to the lineage of the first Shaolin Temple in China, 495 CE. All in their late teens to late twenties, they were honored to be taken as children, far from their birth homes, to the remote Shaoshi Mountain monastery in Henan Province. Their dedication to

1   See the video on YouTube at https://www.youtube.com/watch?v=zDATFToDq94. The man in the video, Sifu Hengyuan, rode the spirited ponies in his native Mongolia until age nine, when he was chosen as an initiate for the monastery.

sixteen-hour days of physical, mental, and spiritual discipline has given the young monks superhuman and paranormal abilities. In public demonstrations, they smash bricks with their hands, shatter steel plates on their heads, and snap spears with the sharp metal tips pressed against their Adam's apples. They will tell you that they accomplish these feats not just with the physical strength of bone and muscle, but through the force of ch'i.

The Origins of Ch'i — Ch'i and the Dao

> *The Dao begins with emptiness.*
> *Extensive emptiness gives birth to the universe.*
> *The universe gives birth to qi.*
> *Qi gives birth to heaven and earth.*

> —Huai Nan Zi, second-century BCE
> Chinese philosophical classic

Ch'i, pronounced "chee" and spelled *qi* in modern Chinese pinyin phonetics, is generally translated as vital energy or life force. (We will use the "ch'i" spelling because it's easier to mentally pronounce as you read this book. See appendix A for a further explanation of qi, ch'i , chi, and ji.)

The character for ch'i — 氣 — first appears in Chinese oracle bone scripts from 1200 BCE, at which time it meant *mist* or the *vapor* from breath on a cold day. The Xing Qi Pei Ming jade carving shown in the photo is a two-inch-tall, twelve-sided cylinder from the late Warring States Period, around 300 BCE. Inscribed with instructions for how to inhale and exhale, it is considered the earliest evidence for the role of ch'i in the theory and practice of qigong. The middle character on the face shown is ch'i.

The metaphysical meaning of ch'i is first recorded in teachings attributed to sixth-century BCE philosopher Lao Tzu (Laozi). Chinese scholars believe Lao Tzu to be a semi-legendary composite of several historical figures from 550 to 350 BCE, mythologized into one man.

In Daoist cosmology, the universe first existed in a state of Nothingness or undifferentiated wholeness — the *Dao* (rhymes with "now"). Numerous philosophies and religions tell a similar story of a primordial condition of no actualities and infinite possibilities. In the Hebrew Kabbalah, the Great Nothingness that preceded the birth of the Universe is the *Ain Sof* (No Thing). In theistic terms, the Dao and the Ain Sof can be imagined as the mind of God before Creation, the universe before the presence of matter.

Another name for the Dao is the *wu ji*, literally the pole-lessness, the formless infinite. From the amorphous, unpolarized wu ji erupted the *tai ji*, the great pole-arity. (See appendix A.) The equivalent astrophysical event was the Big Bang. The tai ji is the crucible for energy and matter and their differentiation into polar opposites, like the north and south poles of a magnet. These opposites, yin and yang, are associated with their respective complementary qualities such as cold and hot, dark and light, wet and dry, contraction and expansion, feminine and masculine. And like the gradual geomagnetic flip of the earth's north and south poles every 300,000 to 800,000 years, yin and yang continually transform into eachother in all of life's processes. Yin and yang are relative to eachother: cold water is yin to the yang of hot water; ice is yin to the yang of cold water.

Ch'i is the organizing principle within the Dao that directs the Nothingness to birth the Somethingness that differentiates into yin and yang. We use the present tense in describing this process, because it is an ongoing cycle of emergence and return.

Forty-seven hundred miles away from the birthplace of Daoism, and contemporary with Lao Tzu, the Greek philosopher Anaximenes expounded on the nature of *aer*, or air, as the stuff of the world. *Aer* evolved into the concept of the *pneuma*, from which we get terms related to the lungs, such as *pneumonia*. Similar in principle to ch'i, *pneuma* also means breath, and in a religious context, spirit or soul. Like ch'i, pneuma is the circulating essence necessary for the functioning of vital organs. The English word *spirit* comes from the Latin *spiritus*, which also means breath. Both the act of inhaling and the eureka! moment of a creative idea, coming as if from the soul, are termed *inspiration*.

Ch'i is the pinyin *qi* in qigong and the Japanese *ki* in aikido and reiki. It is *gi* in Korean and *khí* in Vietnamese. It is *prāṇa* and *kundalini* in Sanskrit, *ruach* in Hebrew, and in Latin, the *animus mundi*, or World Soul. All these terms speak to the unity of the life force, the breath, and the spirit. In contemporary slang, ch'i is your mojo.

Familiarity with the Dao, the wu ji, and the tai ji is important for our practice of qigong. In this melting pot of physiology, philosophy, and spirituality, we will see how the qigong exercises and the method of dan tien breathing described in chapter 10 allow us to experience the interface between body, mind, spirit, and horse. The relationship of breath and ch'i in our bodies and in the horse's body is one of the most important concepts in somatic horsemanship and is key to its benefits for reducing stress.

Energy

In Equine-imity, we talk about our *energy*, the horse's *energy*, and the *energy* between the horses and us. We use the word energy as shorthand for *ch'i* and *reiki*. *Ch'i*, *ki*, and *prāṇa* or *kundalini* are terms used in the martial, healing, and meditative arts to refer to a force that we cannot measure in the way that we can measure electricity, gravity, and heat.

In 2005, the National Center for Complementary and Alternative Medicine (renamed in 2014 the National Center for Complementary and Integrative Health) validated the practice of energy medicine, including qigong. Energy medicine recognizes two types

of energy: *veritable*, which can be measured, and *putative*, which is not yet measurable.

Veritable energies include the calories in food; mechanical vibrations in audible sound and ultrasound; the electromagnetism in light and radio waves; the weak and strong nuclear forces; and gravity. Veritable energies used in medical therapies, such as radiation for cancer, have measurable quantities like wavelength, frequency, and ionizing dose.

In contrast, putative energy fields, also called biofields, have so far eluded quantitation by reproducible methods. Therapies involving putative energy fields are based on theories of healing with ch'i, ki, and reiki and with doshas in Ayurvedic medicine. Other putative forces include prāṇa, kundalini, etheric energy, fohat, orgone, odic force, mana, and homeopathic resonance. Energy medicine practitioners, including doctors of medical qigong, treat their patients empirically using traditional wisdom and a growing body of clinical research. For the purposes of somatic horsemanship, we will adopt at least an imaginal view of ch'i and become open to the warmth and tingling it can produce in our bodies.

The Nature of Ch'i—May the Horse Be with You

For my ally is the Force. And a powerful ally it is.
Life creates it, makes it grow.
Its energy surrounds us and binds us.
Luminous beings are we, not this crude matter.
You must feel the Force around you.
Here, between you, me, the tree, the rock, everywhere!

—Yoda, *Star Wars*

In Daoism, ch'i is the original unseen universal force that manifests as both energy and matter. However, its essence is neither of those and is not wholly definable.

Ch'i suffuses every particle in every living and non-living being throughout the cosmos. It is what causes plants to grow and galaxies to form. It creates weather. It is Leibniz's *entelechy*, the inner drive to self-fulfillment in all living things. It is Freud's and Jung's *libido*, which is not just the sex drive but all creative, generative energies. Ch'i is what Kurt Vonnegut described in *The Sirens of Titan* as the Universal Will to Become. When Albert Einstein proved the equivalency of energy and matter in his formula $E = mc^2$, he gave us a way to see ch'i as both a force and a substance in everything from heavenly bodies to human bodies. In a Discovery Channel documentary, *The Science of Star Wars: War, Weapons and the Force*, the movie's creator, George Lucas, spoke of borrowing concepts from pantheistic (God-in-everything) religions like Daoism. In this interview, Lucas reveals that the idea for the Force came from studying Shaolin monks.

To equate ch'i with energy is to oversimplify it with a meaning that implies it acts like electricity or gravity, which it does not. Ch'i has no weight, no dimensions, no charge, and no calories. As we will see in the qigong exercises, working with one's sense of ch'i and its more spiritual manifestation, reiki, may produce heat, but it is not itself heat. Think of reiki as something like love—an abstract, unquantifiable, unprovable concept that produces physical effects at distances over which electromagnetic fields fall off to zero. Love sent from thousands of miles away causes the heart to beat faster. The EKG can record this rapid heartbeat, but it doesn't measure love. Appendix B is the transcript of a lively panel discussion of physicists and parapsychologists comparing what energy means in physics with what it means in New Age lingo.

Ch'i may be felt as heat, pressure, weight, light, colors, itching, or tingling. These sensations are *transformations* of ch'i into physical qualities rather than ch'i itself. We will use *ch'i* and *reiki* as a shorthand for the forces, however immeasurable, within and beyond our physiological boundaries, that make up our emotions, our subjective energy levels, and all body sensations.

Another matter-energy analogy is the act of thinking of something: say, a horse. The thought produces electrical and chemical changes in the brain. We can see evidence of the thinking process in brain waves on the EEG (electroencephalogram) and on brain scans like the MRI (magnetic resonance image). But these measurements are not the thought itself. Astonishing medical research and reports of near-death and after-death experiences challenge our notions about consciousness, physiology, and energy and suggest that thought and awareness might be energies that reside *outside* the physical brain.[2,3]

Ch'i creates the feelings that we describe in energetic terms. Some days we have good energy, some days nervous energy, and some days we are low energy, though physicists would be at a loss to measure these quantities. When the needle on our energy gauge is hovering near Empty, we may resort to flogging our bodies like tired horses in Western

2   Sam Parnia and Josh Young. *Erasing Death: The Science That Is Rewriting the Boundaries Between Life and Death* (New York: Harper Collins, 2013).

3   Eben Alexander. *Proof of Heaven: A Neurosurgeon's Journey into the Afterlife* (New York: Simon and Schuster, 2012).

movies. We toss down sugary, caffeinated energy drinks with names like Jolt. On the other side of Alice's mushroom are beverages marketed as anti-energy, chill out, or relaxation drinks. These preparations contain calm-down chemicals such as gamma-aminobutyric acid (GABA), melatonin, and California poppy. In the yin and yang of imbibed ch'i manipulation, you can produce your desired energy state with either archetypal bovine: Red Bull or Slow Cow.

The Interface of Ch'i and Breath

The often elusive ch'i is most accessible through the simple process of breathing. In the beginning, it is easier to *feel* breath and *imagine* ch'i. At first, you will feel your breath, and ch'i, as the air that comes into and goes out of your mouth and nose. Gradually, you will learn to imagine, and then feel as if, breath is filling not just the lungs but every part of the body. At that point, you will be feeling ch'i. For simplicity, you can imagine that ch'i and breath are one and the same.

In all somatic arts and athletic activities, and in activities of daily living, proper breathing produces an unimpeded flow of ch'i. Sending breath and ch'i into the outermost and innermost reaches of your body relaxes you when you're tense or over-stimulated, energizes you when you need a lift, and makes your moods less extreme. Breathing into tight muscles is cleansing and invigorating, like wind blowing through freshly washed sheets on a clothesline. Invigoration is the yang to the yin of relaxation. Both are important for stress reduction and emotional regulation.

Horses and Ch'i

Equines are prey animals. They're what's for dinner for several varieties of predators from the dog family (wolves and coyotes), the cat family (mountain lions and, for zebras, jungle cats), and the human family, who hunted horses for food as early as 500,000 BCE, 492,000 years before domesticating them and 496,000 years before riding them. In order to survive as prey for over 60 million years, they evolved exquisite sensitivity to all sensory, and possibly extrasensory, stimuli in their environment.

From any angle within their 357-degree visual field (see the diagram in chapter 1), horses can read the tiniest change in body language—the lowering of a herdmate's head, the swish of his tail, the extension of a single finger from a human fist. Their acute sense of hearing and smell made them reliable sentries for nomads, warriors, and cowboys. When a horse is familiar with a particular human, and sometimes when he meets a human for the first time, he can sense whether the person is happy, tense, angry, or sad. In Traditional Chinese Medicine terms, he is sensing our ch'i. His perceptiveness will help us relate to him and to our own bodies in the course of somatic horsemanship.

Ch'i and Health

Since 320 BCE, theories of yin and yang and ch'i have been the foundation of TCM. In medical qigong, one of the modalities of TCM, there are two kinds of ch'i: the primordial ch'i we were born with and the acquired ch'i that comes from the air we breathe, the food we eat, and the environments in which we live and work. Primordial ch'i was how the ancients described the transmission of genetic material that we now associate with DNA. Chinese geomancy, *feng shui*, addresses environmental ch'i both outdoors and indoors. According to feng shui principles, spaces that are landscaped, enclosed, and furnished so as to promote an optimal flow of ch'i are conducive to love, prosperity, and health.

In TCM, all pain and illness, physical or mental, relate to excess, deficient, or stagnant ch'i. The amount and flow of ch'i within us is affected by internal factors, such as our birth ch'i and emotions, and by external factors such as nutrition, the weather, and other people and animals. Through the use of hair-thin needles (acupuncture), fingers (acupressure), sound (sonopressure), mild electrical stimulation, or burning herbs (moxibustion), TCM practitioners manipulate ch'i along channels called meridians to reduce pain and promote healing. Equine acupuncture, for which most of the meridian maps have been transposed from human pathways, is officially sanctioned by the American Veterinary Medical Association. It has shown good results in hock lameness and other injuries, in moon blindness, and as first aid for colic.

Emotions and feelings of hunger, thirst, and sexual attraction are also states of ch'i. The Chinese term for weather is *tiān ch'i*, sky energy; anger is *shēng ch'i*, rising energy; *xiào ch'i* is laugh energy, the term for nitrous oxide (laughing gas).

The Ch'i Also Rises

Climbing up through the forest to the 11,200-foot Cottonwood Pass in the Eastern Sierra, I am riding a mountain-bred sorrel mule named Sandy. Just over the summit, the trail narrows to two feet wide. It descends at a 40-degree angle on granite steps overlooking a 100-foot drop into the Kern River. For the better part of an hour,

I desperately cling to the imagined connection between my dan tien and Sandy's dan tien. I get unnerved when Sandy, possibly thirsty, periodically peers over the edge to see the river. It is mainly Sandy's sure-footedness and trail savvy, but also perhaps our dan tien melding, that carries us safely down the steep, rocky slope to Horseshoe Meadows.

On that autumn day with the Shaolin monks, their executive director, Master Shi Yanran, sat bareback on Jake. I imagined him to be sinking his dan tien ch'i into Jake's back through his seat bones, as I had done with Sandy, and as I had been doing with all horses.

Over many years of riding lessons, I have worked on strengthening my core and developing a balanced seat. Equitation emphasizes correct weighting of the seat bones and communicating with the abdominal core, thigh, calf, and gluteal muscles. The technique requires keeping your weight low and following your horse's motion. Many horses, especially those trained Western style, can stop on a dime and give nine cents change when the rider just squeezes her butt. Even through a heavy saddle and thick pad, the horse can feel this small contraction. Riding with an independent seat, not hanging on to the reins for balance, is accomplished by correct use of muscles, bones, breath, visualization, and gravity. The energy dynamic is one that allows the horse's power to flow from her hindquarters, like the engine in a VW bug or a Tesla Model S. However, without also mobilizing and blending ch'i, both the horse-human relationship and the resulting motion are restricted.

I asked Master Yanran if I should keep my seat bones weighted with ch'i from my dan tien. Through his translator he replied, "Yes, but you must remember, ch'i goes up as well

Master Yanran on Jake

as down. It does not stay down with the horse." A revelation! It suddenly became clear that in riding, ch'i is meant to circulate around the two bodies, not just keep pulsing down, down, down from my dan tien to the seat bones. Up and down. Down and up. The ch'i also rises.[4]

---

4   There is a further refinement of ch'i rise and fall called the Microcosmic Orbit meditation, which circulates ch'i from the dan tien up the spine, over the head, and down the front midline of the body back to the dan tien. (Some qigong masters advocate starting and ending at the perineum, the area between the anus and genitals.) Flow in the opposite direction, up the front and down the back, is also practiced. Some researchers, and I myself from my past experience with vertigo, theorize that the Microcosmic Orbit corresponds to the three types of tidal undulations — vascular, respiratory, and Sutherland-Upledger waves — of the cerebrospinal fluid. When I am mounted, I additionally include my horse in the Orbit, starting with the energy in her hindquarters.

This Aha! moment has informed my riding, my qigong, and my teaching of both ever since. In the next chapter, we will see how the use of ch'i is expanded by the addition of reiki.

9

Reiki Gong

Ch'i and Reiki Compared

In 1975, while a medical student, I began to practice sitting meditation. I especially worked at meditating without thinking about dinner, spring break, or romance. But it was somewhere between boring and impossible to sit still, watch my breath, and empty my mind.

Many years later, I was delighted to discover moving meditation in the form of tai ji and kung fu.

Then, in the Year of the Horse 2014, I suffered ill effects from improper use of ch'i after overexerting myself in kung fu: several times a day, I had been practicing the strenuous Small Red Fist form in hopes of making the Shaolin team for the San Francisco Chinese New Year parade.

As someone who has always had what Traditional Chinese Medicine calls excess head ch'i—an intensely active mind, frequent headaches, dental and ophthalmic oddities, and wild, frizzy hair—the excess ch'i from overzealous practice went straight to my head. Thus, in bed one night around 3:00 a.m., while mentally rehearsing my kung fu audition, I rolled over and felt the room spin violently. My medical knowledge and objectivity were lost in the throes of half-asleep panic.

What is happening to me?!

In Western medical terms, I was experiencing a classic attack of benign paroxysmal positional vertigo, attributed to displacement of small crystals in the inner ear. In TCM, this symptom is a rare pathological extreme of the normal ch'i awakening of 搖風擺柳 Flowing Breeze, Swaying Willow.

In the years following the initial attack, I have had a few milder episodes. (I prefer to call them *episodes* rather than *attacks.* It's not psychologically healthy to think the body is assaulting us, as in a heart "attack.") In between episodes, I had lingering sensations of movement, like ocean waves, in my head. Acupuncture, medical qigong, the Stanford neurology and vestibular physical therapy clinics, low-impact jogging, and outdoor activities with horses have helped enormously. On a good day, I reckoned I was 88 percent back to normal. However, I was on a quest to be symptom free.[1]

Enter Reiki

Reiki Principles
Just for today,
do not anger,
do not worry.

---

1   I have since regained near normality with the addition of craniosacral therapy, which has proven the ear-crystal model incorrect, or at least not the full story, in my case.

Be filled with gratitude,
be honest in your work,
and be kind to everyone.

—Mikao Usui, *Reiki Founder*

I had been peripherally aware of Reiki for thirty years. It was on my list of Things Probably Too Vague or Far-Fetched to Relate To.

Then just when I was looking to leave no stone unturned in my quest for complete resolution of vertigo, I received a notice about a Reiki attunement with our beloved animal communicator and energy healer, Nancy Windheart. Attunement is the teaching of, blessing for, and initiation into Reiki.

Reiki was developed in 1922 by Japanese Zen Buddhist monk Mikao Usui. In addition to practicing Buddhism, Usui is also reported to have been influenced by Christian studies; one version of his story says he took ordination as a Protestant minister. Reiki has since been passed down through many lineages all over the world. In sharing Reiki, the practitioner draws *ki* ("kee") to herself and then may send it on to another person or animal, or to situations like wars and hurricanes, for healing. The uppermost ideogram of the three Chinese words at the top of this chapter is the character for the rei of reiki. The bottom of the rei character contains the character meaning *wu shaman* 巫. Above that, there are three small squares that each mean *kou*, a mouth: 口口口. They recall the ch'i gulping seen on the ancient pottery at the beginning of chapter 7.

Rei ("ray") is translated as *spirit*, and *ki* is the same as ch'i. So reiki is spiritual energy. The practice of Reiki is akin to the laying on of hands with prayer. Although there are no gold-standard medical studies proving the efficacy of Reiki in healing, there are many anecdotal reports of beneficial effects. There are a few studies showing the efficacy of intercessory prayer. (See Byrd, Reference 1 and Dossey, Reference 5.)

When I received my Reiki Level 1 attunement, I was blown away by the difference between how I sensed reiki compared with how I had always sensed ch'i.[2] The nature of ch'i is taught, and feels to me, as inert, unconscious, unfeeling, finite, and exhaustible when used for martial arts and moving meditation. The nature of reiki for healing is taught, and feels to me, as alive, sentient, compassionate, and infinitely flowing through the body, never to be depleted. With self-reiki and reiki from a massage therapist directed at my vertigo, I felt better than at any time since the symptoms began.

Now more than forty years into my personal evolution, I practice and teach Equine-imity qigong as a synthesis of these two powerful traditions, Chinese and Japanese, in mindfulness, moving meditation, energy cultivation, and healing. As I thought about how to integrate all I have learned, I created this comparison of the ch'i of qigong, tai ji, kung fu, and aikido on one hand and reiki, literally, on the other hand. My practice of tai ji and qigong now includes the gathering and circulation of reiki and sharing reiki with horses.

Ten Points of Comparison of Ch'i and Reiki

1. Ch'i is unconscious, impersonal, value-free, and emotionally neutral. There is no feeling that one is engaged with a sentient being. Ch'i can be cultivated for spiritual enlightenment, but is not itself spiritually enlightened.

---

2   I use Reiki, capital "R," to mean the lineage-based practice and reiki, small "r," to mean the energy itself.

Reiki is conscious and sentient. It has wisdom, compassion, ethics, healing intent, and grace. Some view it as a God-like essence, archangel, or Divine Love.

2. Ch'i is infinite throughout the universe but finite when downloaded to the human body. It can be depleted from one's energy centers with overuse or improper use in advanced practices. The tai ji or qigong practitioner is like a battery storing and discharging electricity. The battery must be constantly recharged.

   Reiki energy is infinite throughout the universe and in the human body. It flows to and through the practitioner, and even when emitted from a person's energy centers, can never be depleted. The Reiki practitioner is like a garden hose channeling water or a water wheel using some energy for its mill and passing the rest on down the river.

3. With emitted qi therapy (EQT), the healer sends out her own ch'i and not, directly, universal ch'i. (See Korahais, Reference 7.)

In Reiki healing, the Reiki practitioner transmits the infinite, universal reiki. We say we are "sharing" reiki, not "giving" reiki.

4. Ch'i used in EQT is directed by the intentions of the healer's ego to cure or fix a person according to the healer's value system, prejudices, biases, and assumptions.

The reiki used in healing is self-directing for the higher good of the recipient. The ego and wishes of the Reiki practitioner do not enter into where or how the energy will be used. The Reiki practitioner cultivates an attitude of "Let go and let God."[3]

5. Ch'i can be used in hand-to-hand combat and to throw or defeat an opponent at a distance.

Reiki always does good, can never be used to oppose, fight, or harm.

6. Overexertion when using ch'i for martial practices can cause significant mental or physical problems. Improperly

---

3   The Western medical practitioner aims to cure the disease; the Traditional Eastern Medicine practitioner aims to cure the person; the Reiki practitioner aims simply to transmit Divine Love.

performed EQT can drain the practitioner and make her ill.[4] Reiki is self-regulating and self-replenishing. It cannot be overused, nor can its use cause illness in the practitioner.

7. Tai ji and qigong practices are done mostly upright, with locomotion of the whole body in patterned forms.

Reiki practice is done lying, sitting, or standing, with small hand gestures and sometimes movement around a treatment table, but no patterned locomotion.

8. In tai ji and qigong, locomotion and in-place limb movements are coordinated with the breath to augment the amount and quality of ch'i.

Reiki gestures are not typically taught in coordination with the breath.

9. Tai ji and qigong have long traditions of study and training. Practitioners, teachers, and healers spend several years, even decades, learning to become proficient at the master level. Tai ji includes competitions, standardization of styles, and oversight by international regulating bodies.

Although rooted in Buddhism, Reiki is a modern tradition. Students are often attuned in weekend courses

4   The chance of experiencing the ill effects I described earlier is effectively zero for the beginning practitioner.

and set out at once to become practitioners. There are no competitions or inter-lineage regulating bodies and no universally accepted standards.

10. Hundreds of credible, peer-reviewed medical studies, some gold standard,[5] have proven the efficacy of tai ji and qigong in healing cancer, arthritis, depression, anxiety, balance impairment, diabetes, high blood pressure, Parkinson's disease, back pain, and other conditions.

There is no body of gold-standard medical studies conclusively proving the efficacy of Reiki.

Qigong, tai ji, and Reiki are complementary to eachother. Qigong and tai ji excel in whole-body coordination of movement, breath, balance, grounding, and energy cultivation. Tai ji can additionally be more active—even explosive—and vigorous. Reiki excels in quiet meditation, the transmission of wisdom and compassion, and the self-replenishing flow of energy for healing. Reiki also emphasizes receiving and transmitting love and gratitude.

Think of the heart. It is both a physical and a metaphysical organ. As a physical organ, it generates electricity. As a metaphysical organ, it generates love. Ch'i is more like the electricity of the heart. Reiki is more like the love.

---

5   The gold standard for medical research includes criteria for a study design that is prospective, randomized, objective, quantitative, and long term. Such a study has control groups and a enough subjects in all groups to test for the statistical significance of differences between the groups and for the strength of the results.

Reiki and Ch'i in Equine-imity

In each person's individual practice, there might not be a felt distinction between ch'i and reiki. In my practices, I feel ch'i primarily as a force within the body and reiki as primarily received from all across the universe. Both forms of energy circulate inside and outside of us. To get the best of both worlds:

1. Imagine reiki as a loving intelligence that comes from the outside in and cannot be depleted.
2. Imagine ch'i as energy that originates in your body, mainly from the lower dan tien.
3. Coordinate your intake and circulation of both reiki and ch'i with movement and breath.
4. Do not be concerned with whether the energies are coming from or going to the right places. Trust that they will direct and cultivate themselves in your body in the way that is optimal for you.
5. Imagine feeling the flow of wise, compassionate, and healing reiki between you and others.

You have now arrived at the point in the book where you can learn the foundational medical qigong practices of Equine-imity, beginning in chapter 10.

References

Byrd RC. Positive therapeutic effects of intercessory prayer in a coronary care unit population. *South Med J*. 1988;81(7):826-829. Randy was a brilliant, compassionate, and highly ethical Cardiology Fellow at (Zuckerberg) San Francisco General Hospital when I was a Family Medicine Resident there.

Catherine Calhoun, L.Ac. Medical Qigong and Reiki http://blog.aoma.edu/Energy-Medicine-Medical-Qigong-and-Reiki.

Jacky Chan. Reiki vs. Qigong. YouTube. 7:43 https://www.youtube.com/watch?v=yD2vuNS9ykg&ab_channel=JackyChan. http://www.taichiqigongreikicentre.com.au.

Mantak Chia and Joyce Thom. *Crianiosacral Chi Kung: Integrating Body and Emotion in the Cosmic Flow*. Rochester, VT: Destiny Books, 2016.

Larry Dossey, MD. *Prayer Is Good Medicine: How to Reap the Healing Benefits of Prayer*. New York: HarperOne, 1997.

Anthony Korahais, The History of Tai Chi. http://flowingzen.com/17970/the-history-of-qigong-and-tai-chi-facts-and-myths/.

Anthony Korahais. Real Stories of External Qi Transmission Part I, 2013. https://flowingzen.com/wp-content/cache/all/9073/external-qi-transmission/index.html.

Ula Moleda, Reiki Master. Qi Gong Practice With Reiki, http://www.reiki-healing-touch.com/&qi_gong

Nancy Windheart, Reiki Master. http://nancywindheart.com

10

POSTURES, POINTS, POWERS, AND GESTURES

*I*n this chapter, you will learn the basic qigong postures and gestures needed for the five Wu Duan Jin forms in the next chapter. The gestures are also stand-alone qigong meditations that can be used for a quick refresher throughout the day, apart from the five forms.

Postures

The Wu Ji Posture—Emptiness, Nothingness, Oneness, and Peace

The wu ji is the great emptiness. It is the original state of the universe and the end state of the bodymind sought in spiritual enlightenment—or at least in the reduction of everyday stress. In the wu ji position, we empty ourselves of mental intrusions and dismiss for the moment any unpleasant emotions.

The posture for the wu ji position, like *Tadasana* mountain pose in yoga, is upright and relaxed. In the wu ji posture, we are in a state of no contrasts, no conflicts, no distractions. Imagine you are a string of pearls hanging from the sky. Or feel yourself as a grape suspended in a Jell-O mold. The spine is stretched up and tall. Each vertebral segment is elongated so that the *Ming Men*, the Gate of Life in the small of your back, is allowed to stretch and open. Shoulders are relaxed, drawn down by the weight of your arms. Arms hang loosely by your sides. The chest is open; the emotional heart is open. Knees are soft. Do not lock your knees; you can bend them slightly, or simply unlock them. Your buttocks are gently tucked in, not sticking out in a sway-backed frame. Go into the wu ji barefoot or in flat shoes. The higher the heels of your shoes, the harder it is to have soft knees while keeping your spine in alignment.

Qigong adepts can meditate in the wu ji position for up to an hour. In one variant, the practitioner holds her rounded arms out from the body, as if encircling a giant beach ball or a tree.

Horses find the most comfortable posture of least resistance and least effort. While they often nap lying on the ground, most of their sleep time is spent on their feet. The *stay apparatus* in their lower limbs allows them to sleep while standing hipshot, cocking a rear leg for long periods of time without muscle fatigue or collapse. A horse is a qigong adept who can stand in the wu ji for hours.

We return to the wu ji posture after each form of the wu duan jin.[1] We stay in the wu ji as we walk to the horses for

---

1   In case you're wondering, the "wu" (none, nothingness) of the wu ji and the "wu" (five) of the wu duan jin are not the same word.

meet and greet and for performing the dan tien press and the dan tien hug.

The Tai Ji

From the undifferentiated universe of the wu ji, we enter the
tai ji,[2] the realm of constantly
changing yin and yang forces
in balanced opposition. The tai
ji can be experienced somatically as the yang of inhaling
and the yin of exhaling.

Soft Eyes

Each posture and gesture in qigong is accompanied by the mindful use of the eyes. We strive for a way of seeing that is focused yet panoramic. The late Sally Swift, author of the equitation classic *Centered Riding*, describes this way of seeing as soft eyes.

> Relax your eyes. Let an object be the general center of your gaze, but look at it with your peripheral vision taking in the largest possible expanse, above and below as well as to the left and right. Have the feeling of going within yourself. It becomes clear that soft eyes are much more than just a way of looking. Using soft eyes is like

---

2   *Tai ji* is often spelled *t'ai chi* or *tai chi. Chi* is pronounced "ji" and is not the same as *ch'i* (qi, "chee") meaning life force energy. (See appendix A.)

a new philosophy. It is a method of becoming distinctly aware of what is going on around you, beneath you, inside of you.[3]

For a blind person, as well as for the sighted, the same attentiveness applies to hearing, smell, things felt on the skin, and internal sensations. Listen to the birds and the wind and the breathing of the horses. Feel the sun and the bugs on your skin. Become aware of everything and yet distracted by nothing that does not require action. If you hear an engine roar in the middle of your meditation, be aware but not annoyed. Learn detached awareness from horses, who are aware of much more than we think, and who act only when necessary.

Dream and Buck—A Lesson in Soft Eyes

It is dusk on a cold afternoon in the first week of November. The sun setting behind the mountain lion habitats of Jasper Ridge has burned out the last of its reds and oranges. We are left with dimly lit purple-grays. I am usually off-ranch at this hour, and not used to the new man-made evenings of "falling back" to standard time. The rains came early this year, and the horses churned up their summer pasture into a muddy swamp. So they have been herded onto the polo field for their annual winter relocation. More than sixty horses are quietly eating their hay along the edge of the field, which lies inside a half-mile oval dirt track. The older, thinner, and clipped horses are blanketed. All their bodies, covered and bare, blur into masses indistinct in the twilight.

As I walk just outside the track, I spot my horse Dream's bright white coat. She is head down in hay about thirty feet from me, a little

---

3   Sally Swift. *Centered Riding.* Trafalgar Square Farm Book (North Pomfret, VT: David & Charles, 1985).

way into the field. There are several horse shapes between us, and she evidently hasn't noticed my little gray shape coming from off to her side. Suddenly Buck, an aggressively social and treat-seeking gelding, comes running toward me in a way I find threatening. And puzzling—I have never handed him food! In the next nanosecond, Dream charges out of what I assumed to be unawareness and runs Buck off, saving me from his assault. It is incredible to me that she has been attentive all along, not only to me, but to Buck, in the distance, in the dark.

Dream taught me that soft eyes isn't just a visual field; it's a total awareness field of sight, sound, smell, and instinct.

Energy Points and Centers

The Bubbling Spring Yong Quan Foot Centers

Yong quan ("yoong chwan") means a *bubbling*, or *gushing*, *spring*. The yong quan Bubbling Springs energy centers are located near the balls of the feet, between the second and third toes, where they are said to *ground* our ch'i. Just like the ground wire in an electrical circuit, the Bubbling Springs centers drain excess ch'i into the earth where it can't build up to create a shock, or disease, within our bodies. Sensing our feet firmly touching the ground is a technique for releasing excess or unpleasant energies resulting from overactive thinking and emoting. The Bubbling

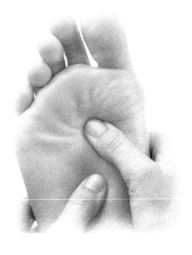

Springs center is the first point on the Kidney meridian in Traditional Chinese Medicine. It is used in acupressure and reflexology to relieve headaches, dizziness, and insomnia that might result from having too much ch'i stagnating in the head.

Place your feet firmly on the ground and feel yourself connected to the earth through the Bubbling Springs. The more you focus on where your feet touch the ground, the less top-heavy you will feel from the weight of a worried mind or a troubled heart. If you have a distracting thought, send it down through the Bubbling Springs centers, down into the earth. This technique is called grounding. It feels especially good in bare feet on a beach where the tide meets the shore. The cool, wet sand is yin to the excess yang of turbulent thoughts and fiery emotions, especially anger.

When you stand beside a horse, you can imagine grounding through all six of your combined legs. When you sit on a horse, this tandem grounding is even easier to feel. You will ground through the parts of your body that touch the horse—buttocks, crotch, inner thighs, lower legs—down through the horse's barrel, legs, and feet.

Spend a few minutes each day in walking meditation, where you imagine that with each step you take, you kiss the earth with your feet. Meditative walking differs from our usual purposeful walking in that with meditation, we are not thinking of getting somewhere. We move slowly and mindfully, focusing within our bodies and appreciating the natural beauty surrounding us. Circular labyrinths laid out in public parks and on church and temple grounds are especially peaceful for walking meditation. Not to be confused with mazes, labyrinths provide a single path into and out from the center of the circle, without barriers or dead ends. Deep grounding comes from walking barefoot in a labyrinth.

When we ride horses in a saddle, the horizontal bar of the stirrup passes directly under the Bubbling Springs, as shown in the illustrations. In this way, the Bubbling Springs become another center for grounding through the horse's legs.

 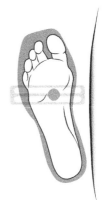

The horse's energy centers, which correspond to the Bubbling Springs in our feet and the Lao Gong centers in our palms, connect horses to the earth through all four limbs. You will learn to ground and center yourself using all the energy centers in the feet and bellies—yours and your horse's—when you are beside or on your horse.

The Palace of the Heart Lao Gong Palm Centers

In qigong and Reiki practice, the Lao Gong centers in the palms of the hands are powerful emitters of energy for healing the self and others, including animals. *Lao gong* is often translated as *Palace of Toil*. In acupressure, the Lao Gong center is the 8th point on the Pericardium meridian, which ends at the tips of the middle fingers.

In both Western medicine and TCM, the pericardium

protects the heart. Hence, the Lao Gong is also known as the *Palace of the Heart*. In TCM, the pericardium not only provides physical protection, but it also protects the heart from damage by excessive emotional energies generated by the other organs, such as anger from the liver, fear from the kidneys, and grief from the lungs.

Charging up the palms with the Taking the Sun Down from the Sky and Open and Close gestures described below imparts power to the pericardium as a physical and meta-physical protector of the heart.

Powers

The Dan Tien

People spend years searching for the dan tien, but never find it.
Many give up, convinced that the dan tien is
either mystical mumbo jumbo or a metaphor.
I was one of them.
For years, I was thinking, "Where in the world is the dan tien?"
Even after I met [my Master Teacher]
and learned the real secrets of energy cultivation,
and practiced for a few years,
I still didn't feel anything.

—Sifu Anthony Korahais, Tai Ji and Qigong Master

The lower *dan tien* ("dahn tyen") shown in the drawings is one of three dan tien centers of vital energy, similar to the yogic concept of chakras. The lower dan tien corresponds to the Svadhisthana, or second, chakra in yoga, the hara in aikido, and the core in Pilates. When we speak of the dan tien, we are referring to the lower center.

The dan tien is the fountainhead of personal power. Its archetype is the Warrior. Its potency fires up the elements of one's *agency*: integrity, conviction, strength of character, bravery, and self-determination. Speaking with a weak, soft voice and acting timidly are the antitheses of dan tien power. One must learn to speak, sing, walk, paint, cook, dance, play piano, ride horses, and perform all other actions from the dan tien. The history of longstanding, unavenged abuses culminating in the #MeToo movement was a crisis in dan tien powerlessness. Acting heroically from the dan tien results in the courage to say #MeFirst as an initiator, a leader.

The horse's dan tien is located under our seat. When we perform the dan tien press and the dan tien hug described in chapter 13, and when we sit astride a horse, we share our dan tien powers.

Gestures

Inner Smile Qigong

The Inner Smile is a simple Daoist meditation on how to live with an open heart. It is a subtle gesture in which we smile inwardly to each of the organs of our body and feel them smiling back. Smiling from within activates the energy of loving-kindness, especially toward ourselves.

We use it early and often in all our qigong gestures, when performing the Wu Duan Jin forms, and while engaged in everyday activities. The Inner Smile trains us to uncondition-ally accept every aspect of our body, mind, and spirit. It restores the natural impulse to smile that we had as babies. It doesn't try to fix us or challenge our basic goodness. It simply asks us to use compassion and equanimity to look upon every living being and every situation. Some people get stuck in a chronic inner frown state. By consciously and repeatedly trading the frown for the smile, the smile state will predominate and become second nature.[4]

Imagine all your organs have a sweet little smile. You smile at them, and they smile back. Then, turn up the corners of your mouth in a little smile. Breathe deeply. Continue to smile. Breathe deeply.

Dan Tien Breathing

To experience the opposing, yet balanced, forces of the tai ji somatically, we use the inhalation and exhalation of dan tien breathing. With each inhalation, we allow the belly to expand, becoming full and round and soft. We exhale from the dan tien down through the Bubbling Springs centers, setting up a smooth, rhythmic circulation of breath, ch'i, and reiki.

Nervous breathing is rapid and shallow, involving mostly the upper chest. Slow, deep, dan tien breathing fills the entire

---

4   Michael Winn. *Way of the Inner Smile Self-Acceptance Tao Path to Inner Peace.* https://healingtaousa.com/wp-content/uploads/pdf/innersmile_ch01.pdf

chest and belly.[5] Dan tien breathing might be especially challenging, and yet freeing, for women who have been culturally conditioned to display flat, sucked-in bellies. A contracted belly prevents the deep breathing that minimizes stress.[6] Slow breathing also slows the heart rate, which in turn lowers blood pressure.

Breath, and the ch'i and reiki that flow with it, must be allowed to rise and fall gently between the sky, the head, the chest, the lower dan tien, the Bubbling Springs in the feet, and the earth.

The Earth and Sky Reiki Cleanse

With Open and Close, shown on the next page, the Earth and Sky reiki cleanse is one of the two most basic gestures in learning to coordinate breathing with muscle movements. Using a sweeping motion with arms extended from the sides, imagine gathering reiki from the earth, and then from the sky. Think of it as making a snow angel while standing up. Cleanse your mind and body with reiki, then drain the wash "water" back into the ground through your Bubbling Springs. Imagine that any unwanted thoughts and emotions you wash away get taken up by the earth like fertilizer for the grass and trees and flowers.

---

5   Of course, air doesn't really enter the belly unless we have a punctured lung! However, relaxing the abdominal muscles allows us to breathe more deeply, with more downward movement of the diaphragm and expansion of the entire chest and abdominal cavities.

6   Toned musculature in the abdomen, such as is achieved with bodybuilding or Pilates, is not a sucked-in belly. It is possible to have increased muscle tone and mass while still relaxing into softness and fullness during dan tien breathing.

Earth and Sky Reiki Cleanse

Step 1

Step 3

Step 4

Step 5

1. Start in the wu ji position, arms at your sides (see photo).
2. Draw reiki from the earth, through your fingertips, up into your hands.
3. Using your dan tien breathing, slowly inhale as you sweep your arms out to the sides, palms up, then above your head (see photo).
4. When your arms are stretched overhead, the palms face eachother, fingers pointing to the sky (see photo).
5. Slowly exhale as you bend your forearms, facing your palms down, pushing the reiki down through the front of your body — past your face, chest, dan tien, and legs (see photo).
6. In the same exhalation, push the reiki down through the Bubbling Springs, into the earth, until your arms are hanging down again in wu ji position.
7. Repeat these snow angel sweeps a few times until you feel rinsed and refreshed.

In chapter 6 we noted a groundbreaking study by Chin and Kales that shows that muscle motion combined with rhythmic breathing is more effective for stress reduction than either limb movement or relaxation breathing by themselves.

Gassho/Anjali Mudra

Pressing the palms together in prayer or greeting is common in many religions and cultures. In yoga practice, this hand position (mudra) is called the anjali (AHN-jah-lee) mudra, often accompanied by the Hindi word *namaste*. The gesture and the utterance mean "the Divine in me embraces the Divine in you."

In Reiki practice, this gesture is called *Gassho* ("gah-show"), Japanese for "hands together." Gassho clears the mind, opens the heart, and prepares the body to receive reiki.

Shi De Yang, one of the most venerated Shaolin masters alive today, explains this gesture as a way to gather and emit ch'i. We characterize these emissions as *ling ch'i* (Chinese) or *reiki* (Japanese), both meaning spiritual energy. Starting in wu ji posture, Shi De Yang says, "First I raise my hands slowly overhead. This is done to regulate the ch'i. Gather all the air in the centers of both palms and bring them together above the head, like holding a ball. Compress the ball until your hands meet and put it in front of the chest. Exhale dispassionately. This is not simply the hand salute greeting of Buddhism. It is really a way of gathering the ch'i from nature. I use it to give health to others and to all of you. Its most important sense is to give the ch'i in our body to others."[7]

---

7   See a video of Shi De Yang performing this gesture on YouTube at https://www.youtube.com/watch?v=2KevHM5oJ2k, minute 4:00.

Taking the Sun Down from the Sky, Open and Close

Open and Close is a basic movement in many classical qigong and tai ji forms. With the Earth and Sky Cleanse, it is the simplest gesture for learning to coordinate muscle motion with breathing and ch'i circulation. Its purpose is also to receive and concentrate reiki in the hands from where it can be sent to one's own body and those of others.

Open and Close

To begin, use the gesture for Taking the Sun Down from the Sky: reach up for the sun and imagine pulling it down to your heart level. Hold your hands in Gassho and imagine the sun you are holding is a warm ball of wise, compassionate, and healing reiki.

Then imagine the reiki sun expanding in your hands, pushing them out to shoulder width apart (see photo). Move your hands back into Gassho, compressing the sun into a denser ball. Repeat the cycle, inhaling as your hands spread apart and exhaling as they return to Gassho. After a few cycles, as you charge up the Palace of the Heart centers, your hands may become warm and tingly. End the Open and Close cycles by inhaling deeply, spreading your hands out to shoulder width. Exhale as you drop your hands slowly, slowly down to your sides, allowing your ch'i to flow back to the earth and back to the wu ji.

Both the Earth and Sky Cleanse and Open and Close are calming gestures that can take you back to grazing, back to equanimity. They can be performed throughout the day, lying down, sitting, or standing—at your desk, in the yard, on the toilet—any time you need the pause that refreshes. You can perform them before going into a meeting, a stressful social gathering, or a public speaking engagement. You can do Open and Close in your car at a stop light. You will perform both gestures several times in the Wu Duan Jin qigong forms with and on your horse.

These are the core qigong movements of Equine-imity as performed with and by ourselves. In Part IV we include the horse.

11

The Wu Duan Jin

Five Silken Movements

The Ba Duan Jin is one of the medical qigong sets most often practiced for health benefits. Deceptively simple, the set of eight forms is performed, often daily, by every type of person from young, muscular Shaolin monks in ancient temples to the elderly in public parks. It is enjoyed by people at all levels of physical ability and spiritual development. The name is usually translated as Eight Sections of Brocade. We can imagine that the brocades are medieval tapestries—I think of the intricate seven-section *Hunt of the Unicorn*—in which each weaving tells a story about the form's meaning for health and longevity. The Ba Duan Jin is also known as the Eight Silken Movements. Silken aptly describes the soft, flowing motions of the limbs and breath.

The origin of the Eight Brocades is clothed in mystery. It is said to have developed from the I Ching philosophy of yin and yang balance, dating back to 1000 BCE. A similar exercise is documented in Chinese literature from the Wei and Jin dynasties (220 CE to 289 CE). Legend has it that General Yue Fei taught the Ba Duan Jin to his soldiers in the twelfth century CE, 500 years before tai ji was documented as a martial art.

The Ba Duan Jin made a comeback in China in 2004 with the establishment of the Chinese Health Qigong Association. The association's purpose is to promote qigong nationwide, based on growing scientific evidence for its health benefits. In 2013, a modern interpretation of the Ba Duan Jin set was promoted by the General Administration of Sport of China, expanding its popularity for community health programs. The Health Qigong Association endorses the Ba Duan Jin for muscular strength, body-trunk-eye coordination, and emotional self-regulation. Randomized controlled clinical trials have shown that the Ba Duan Jin can strengthen musculoskeletal fitness, reduce depression, and improve blood circulation, sleep, and quality of life measures.

The Wu Duan Jin

In Ba Duan Jin, *ba* means eight. Of the eight classical forms, five can be performed on horseback. Five in Chinese is *wu*, so we call our Equine-imity set the Wu Duan Jin. Like the basic gestures we learned in the previous chapter, the Wu Duan Jin coordinates dan tien breathing with gentle muscle movement.

I have kept the instructions simple so that:

- They are easy to learn, especially from a book.
- They prevent obsession with the right and wrong way to do the forms. There is no one right way that suits all bodies.
- They let you focus on your breathing, which is the most important element.
- They leave gaps and ambiguities that encourage you to experiment with what feels best to you.

These five forms, or just your favorites among them, can become the basis of a daily moving meditation practice and can be integrated with other forms of exercise. I like to do tai ji or qigong before and after I run, when I first go into the arena on my horse, or standing next to her while she grazes. Preferably, you will do the exercises outdoors, and ideally, you will do them in the company of horses. The Equine-imity video at https://youtu.be/49PiUYifhUs shows each form of the Wu Duan Jin on the ground and on horseback.[1]

We will attribute to each form the health benefits for its respective organ in accordance with the principles of Traditional Chinese Medicine. In the TCM worldview, organ designations are not identical to the anatomical structures of Western medicine. The TCM Heart is not simply a physical organ. It's a metaphysical concept referring to an organ *system* and its associated flavors, colors, emotions, and seasons. These organ systems are networked by energy channels, called meridians, used in acupuncture and other healing modalities.

Dan Tien Breathing for the Wu Duan Jin

The type of breathing needed to raise the ch'i for the Wu Duan Jin is the dan tien, or abdominal, breathing introduced in the previous chapter. To better understand dan tien breathing, lie on your back on a hard surface and place a paper plate on your abdomen. (This is the only exercise in this book that

---

1   Note that the instructions here differ somewhat from what you will see in the video. For example, most of the forms are performed in horse-riding stance. And from my experience with hundreds of students, the Wu Duan Jin evolved to include more Open and Close and Gassho gestures between and within the forms. In addition, the forms in the video and as taught in class are slightly more complex. I have simplified them for the ease of use in this book.

is not safe to do next to a horse!) Inhale so as to lift the plate toward the ceiling or sky. The motion is one of "puffing out your stomach" with your breath. You might only be able to move the plate half an inch or less.

Then try it standing up, using your hand instead of a plate. Place your hand lightly on your abdomen and inhale so as to push your hand out from your body. Keep your shoulders down and relaxed. Of course, you are not actually breathing into your belly; you are still breathing into your lungs, which are in your chest. However, a relaxed, ballooned-out belly allows your diaphragm to descend deeper into the abdominal cavity. The pulled-down diaphragm creates a vacuum into which air rushes to fill your lungs. With dan tien breathing, the lungs can expand to their maximum volume. Visualizing air going where it doesn't literally, physiologically go is the key to feeling ch'i. By imagining the air we breathe flowing everywhere in the body, we imagine, then feel, the flow of ch'i and reiki.

In general, we inhale when the body is expanding and the limbs are making upward and outward motions. We exhale when the body is contracting and the limbs are making downward and inward motions. In the forms below, inhale when raising the arms and gathering reiki with the hands and exhale while lowering the arms, when pointing, and when punching. Inhaling is yang, filling; exhaling is yin, emptying. However, as with all things yin and yang, the qualities of up and down, expansion and contraction, force and gentleness, are relative. For instance, in Hold Up the Sky, we exhale when pushing upward to release anxiety, even though the arms are expanding. In Punch with an Angry Gaze, we exhale forcefully with the punch even though the arm is extending. In kung fu and the martial forms of tai ji, striking motions, like chopping and punching, are accompanied by exhaling and are yang in their thrusting nature.

Use your soft eyes, as taught in the previous chapter, to follow the active hand in each form. While focusing on your hand, stay aware of everything in your peripheral vision.

Although I present the Wu Duan Jin forms as they are classically taught, there is no one right way to do them. There are variant Ba Duan Jin practices ranging from a few minutes to half an hour or more. The most important thing is for you to feel the free flow of breath, and therefore ch'i and reiki, while you make your silken movements. If you have any physical limitations, you must modify the forms according to your abilities. A rule of thumb is to never exceed 70 percent of your maximum range of motion in turning and reaching. Stay within your comfort zone; you might see how that boundary stretches with regular practice. While you're learning to coordinate breath and gestures, you may need to take more or fewer breaths than are called for in the instructions.

There is a much more fluid transition between the forms than the instructions imply. The silken quality will emerge as you get more familiar with the set as a whole. To that end, I suggest you learn the movements as I teach them in class:

1. First learn the mechanics of the movements.
2. Then add the coordinated cycles of inhaling and exhaling.
3. Finally, add the release of unwanted emotions and the gathering of desired emotions.

The Wu Duan Jin Forms

Refer to the previous chapter for the basics of using Soft Eyes and performing the Earth and Sky Cleanse, Gassho, and Open and Close gestures incorporated in the following forms.

Form 1—Hold Up the Sky

The TCM-attributed benefits of Hold Up the Sky are to help the Adrenal system recover from the hormonal outpouring of the fight-or-flight response and to relieve symptoms of ADHD, anxiety, panic attacks, insomnia, and tinnitus (TIN-it-us—ringing in the ears). While performing the gestures, imagine releasing anxiety and gathering calm. (See photos of this exercise following these instructions.)

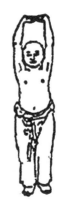

1. Start in the wu ji position, arms by your sides.
2. Bring your hands together, palms up, under your dan tien, fingertips touching (see photo).
3. (Inhale) Lift your arms and hands vertically in front of you.
4. (Continue to inhale) As your arms come to chest level, your forearms will naturally turn your palms toward you (see photo).
5. (Exhale) As you continue lifting your arms, roll your hands in toward your face. When your hands are at eye level, your thumbs will point down (see photo).
6. (Continue to exhale) Continue to roll your hands so that your palms face up to the sky when you extend your

arms, as shown in the drawing and photo. Thumbs will be facing front (see the drawing of the monk and the photo).

7. (Complete the exhale) Press the sky gently, as if it's depending on you to hold it up. Stretch! —but keep a little bend in your elbows. In TCM, locked joints block the flow of ch'i, causing stagnation that leads to disease. If you have no neck limitations, follow your hands with your eyes and look up at the sky as you stretch. We spend most of our lives looking at eye level or below. Remember to look up at the sky and clouds and tops of trees! *Use this exhale to release anxiety.*

8. (Inhale) Cup your hands and twirl them as if scooping ice cream out of the sky. You are gathering reiki (see photo).

9. (Continue to inhale) Bring your hands and arms downward, palms slightly facing eachother. Imagine drawing reiki down to wash over you, as in the Earth and Sky Cleanse.
Use this inhale to take in calmness and equanimity.

10. Bring your hands into Gassho and exhale.

Hold Up the Sky

Step 2   Step 4   Step 5

Step 6   Step 8

Form 2—Shoot the Arrow

This form is traditionally known as Shoot the Hawk, but for Equine-imity, we don't foster images of violence to animals. (We *feed* two birds with one *seed* and don't *feed* a dead horse.) Even when done on the ground, this form uses the horse-riding stance, which was the position of ancient Chinese mounted warriors. The TCM-attributed benefits of Shoot the Arrow are for the Kidney system, which is damaged by strong or chronic fear.

While performing the gestures, imagine releasing fear and gathering courage. Imagine also that you are shooting down any obstacles that keep you from receiving all the wonderful things you deserve. Think of a scenario in which you hunt and bag as a trophy anything you have wished for—health, prosperity, satisfying work, clarity of consciousness, peace. You might even pretend that you are Cupid shooting for love in all its forms. In Shooting the Arrow, Buddhists aim for wisdom, health, vitality, longevity, and freedom from the cycle of reincarnation. Taoists, Christians, Jews, Muslims, Hindus, pagans, and atheists might aim for some principle or quality consistent with the highest ideals of those traditions.

1. At the end of Hold Up the Sky, you have exhaled into Gassho in wu ji posture.
2. Place your feet shoulder width apart and sink down a couple of inches into horse-riding stance. (Do not try to sink as low as the monk in the drawing!)

Shoot the Arrow

Steps 2 and 3

Step 4

Step 6A

Step 6B

At the same time, cross your wrists at chest level, palms facing you (see photo).

3. Make a soft fist with your right hand; point the index finger of your left hand (see photo).

4. (Inhale) Pull your hands and arms apart as if drawing a bow string. The right arm will remain bent at chest level as shown in the drawing of the monk and the photo.

5. (Exhale) Extend your left arm out to the side and point the finger. Imagine your breath and ch'i are flowing down your arm and out through your fingertip. Follow your finger with your eyes.

   Use this exhale to release fear.

6. (Inhale) Sweep your outstretched left arm in front of your body (see photo 6A), through a 180-degree (half circle) arc, until your fingertip touches the right elbow (see photo 6B).

   Use this inhale to gather courage.

7. Repeat steps 4 through 6 with the left arm drawing the bow and the right arm pointing the arrow.

8. (Big, deep inhale) Bring your legs together and stand in wu ji posture as you perform the Earth and Sky Cleanse.

9. Bring your hands into Gassho and exhale.

While the arm gestures coordinated with the breath cleanse the Kidney system, the horse stance works the thigh, calf, and buttocks muscles to improve lower body strength. The side-to-side gestures in horse stance develop balance and coordination. The imagery of snagging the objects of your desire with your arrows restores a childlike sense of play to any overly stern goal orientation and stimulates the power of positive thinking.

Form 3—Separate Heaven and Earth

 This form gives you a nice stretch that elongates the Spleen and Stomach meridians and benefits their associated organs and energies. It facilitates dan tien breathing and relieves tension in the chest, back, and shoulder muscles. Emotions that damage the Stomach and Spleen system include sadness, depression, and loneliness. While performing the gestures, imagine releasing sadness and gathering contentment.

As you separate heaven from earth, the motion of the arms creates a dynamic balance of yin and yang. When the arms go in opposite directions, one arm is yin and one arm is yang. But which is which? It's all relative. Generally, left is yin and right is yang. However, that which is up, nearer heaven, is yang and down, nearer earth, is yin. So if your left arm is up, is it yin or yang? Ch'i is yang and blood is yin. But the fullness and warmth of blood in the veins of the down-hanging arm is yang, and the drained, bloodless state of the up-reaching arm is yin. So if your right arm (yang) is up nearer heaven (yang) and bloodless (yin), is it yin or yang?

The relativity of yin and yang applies to the changing emotional and energetic states within yourself and with respect to others around you. Perhaps you consider yourself an outgoing conversationalist (yang). But when you meet a loud, boisterous, nonstop talker, you might feel comparatively reserved (yin).

1. At the end of Shoot the Arrow, you have exhaled into Gassho in wu ji posture.

2. (Inhale) Spread your hands to shoulder width apart as in Open and Close.

3. (Exhale) Extend the left arm and hand up to the sky, palm up, and the right arm and hand down toward the earth, palm down like the monk in the drawing. As you separate your arms, turn your head and neck to 70 percent of their maximum range of motion, facing toward the shoulder of the downward-reaching arm. Keep your shoulders down and relaxed. Do not shrug the shoulder of the upward-reaching arm. Gently stretch right and left arms up and down respectively. *Use this exhale to release sadness.*

4. (Inhale) Cup your hands and twirl them as if scooping ice cream.

5. (Continue to inhale) Bring your hands into Gassho. *Use this inhale to gather happiness.*

6. Exhale in Gassho.

7. Repeat steps 2 through 6 with the right hand and arm going up, the left going down.

Form 4—Wise Old Owl Looks Around

TCM prescribes Wise Old Owl to relieve energy depletion, stiff muscles along the spine, "pinched" nerves, and back pain. It is also used to ward off premature aging. While performing the gestures, imagine releasing fatigue and gathering vitality.

In Five Animal Frolics qigong, the practitioner takes on the qualities and spirit of each of the five animals in its respective frolic. We are invited to do the same in the Wu Duan Jin. The archetypal power of Owl is wisdom. She can turn her head almost 180 degrees left and right. Her wisdom comes from being able to see all sides of a situation. As you gently and slowly turn your head from side to side, staying within your comfort zone, enjoy the different points of view throughout your range of vision.

1. At the end of Separate Heaven and Earth, you have exhaled in Gassho in wu ji posture.
2. (Inhale) Spread your hands to shoulder width apart as in Open and Close.
   Slowly lower your arms to your sides.
3. (Exhale) Turn slowly at the waist to face right, eyes sweeping the horizon (see the drawing of the monk). Turn gently to 70 percent of your maximum range of motion.
   Use this exhale to release fatigue.
4. (Inhale) Turn back to facing front.
   Use this inhale to take in vitality.
5. Repeat steps 2 and 3 to the left.
6. (Big deep inhale) Do the Earth and Sky Cleanse.
7. Bring your hands into Gassho and exhale.[2]

Form 5—Punch with an Angry Gaze

This form, our longest, teaches the slow, controlled release of anger. In TCM, anger injures the Liver system. This injury may manifest as excess Liver wind in the head, causing headaches, vertigo, and visual and hearing disturbances. Social scientist and empathy pioneer Karla McLaren, M.Ed.,

2   A more authentic version of this form, as performed in class, is shown in the video (https://youtu.be/49PiUYifhUs). It entails turning side to side with one hand cupping the back of the head and one hand on the Ming Men Life Gate in the lower back.

identifies more than fifty shades of anger. Crankiness, bigotry, frustration, irritation, impatience, disgust, intolerance, hatred, spite, and sarcasm are all on the anger spectrum.[3] Punch with an Angry Gaze benefits the Liver system by dispersing anger and assimilating acceptance, patience, tolerance, understanding, and compassion. While performing the gestures, imagine releasing all gradations of anger and gathering the antidotes to any of their expressions.

In projecting an Angry Gaze, your face assumes a fierce expression, like ancient Chinese demons. You are learning to scowl with dignity and determination. In TCM, strong ch'i is emitted through the eyes. This is one reason that both prey animals like horses and predators like dogs may interpret staring into their eyes as aggression.

Qigong Master Effie Poy Yew Chow, RN, PhD, teaches that, whereas most other Ba Duan Jin forms pantomime exposure and vulnerability, Punch with an Angry Gaze and Shoot the Arrow are rituals of power and protection.

In steps 1 through 8, follow the punching fist with your soft eyes.

1. At the end of Wise Old Owl Looks Around, you have exhaled into Gassho in wu ji posture.
2. (Inhale) Bring both hands to your sides at waist level, palms up. Elbows are bent. At the same time, spread your feet to shoulder width apart and sink into horse-riding stance (see photo).
3. (Exhale) Turn your right hand over, make a fist, and punch out in front of you in a slow, controlled manner (see photo).

---

3 Karla McLaren. *The Art of Empathy: A Complete Guide to Life's Most Essential Skill* (Boulder, CO: Sounds True, 2013).

Use this exhale to release disappointment.

4. (Inhale) Open your fist; cup and twirl your hand like scooping ice cream. Still inhaling, bring the right hand slowly back to your waist, palm up.
   Use this inhale and scooping motion to gather acceptance.
   At the end, both hands will be at your waist, palms up as in Step 2.

5. Repeat steps 3 and 4 with your left fist.
   Use the exhale to release impatience.
   Use the inhale to gather patience.
   At the end, both hands will be palms up at your waist.

6. (Exhale) Make a fist with the right hand and punch out to the right side, looking at your fist (see photo Step 6).
   Use this exhale to release intolerance.

7. (Inhale) Open your fist; cup and twirl your hand like scooping ice cream.

8. Still inhaling, bring your hand slowly back to your waist, palm up. At the end, face front with your hands at your waist, palms up, as in Step 2.
   Use this inhale to gather tolerance.

9. Repeat Steps 6 and 7 with the left hand.
   Use the exhale to release hypercriticalness.
   Use the inhale to gather understanding.

10. Repeat Steps 6 and 7, punching to the sides with both fists at once, looking straight ahead.
    Use the exhale to release anger.
    Use the inhale to gather compassion.
    Finish with both hands at your waist, palms up.

Punch with an Angry Gaze

Step 2

Step 3

Step 6

11. (Big deep inhale) Bring your legs together and stand in wu ji posture as you perform the Earth and Sky Cleanse. Bring your hands into Gassho and exhale.

12. Spend some quiet moments in the wu ji.

Summary of the Five Releases and Five Gathers

This table summarizes the negative emotions that are released in the Wu Duan Jin during exhalation and the positive emotions that are inhaled in their place.

Form	Organ System	Releases	Gathers
Hold Up the Sky	Adrenals	Anxiety	Calm, equanimity
Shoot the Arrow	Kidney	Fear	Courage
Separate Heaven and Earth	Stomach/ Spleen	Sadness	Happiness, contentment
Wise Old Owl	Spine	Fatigue	Vitality
Punch with an Angry Gaze	Liver	Anger	Forgiveness, tolerance, understanding, compassion

Part IV

The Stanford Equine-imity Four Phase Program

Introduction

The chapters in this section provide instructions for the activities that have been taught in Equine-imity in the Stanford Health Improvement Program since 2013. The directions are simplified with the assumption that you will follow them under the guidance of a professional horsemanship instructor or a trusted friend with equine expertise. Choose a person who is both competent and kind. Appendix C will help you find horse people and horse programs.

To the extent that these skills have recreational value, and to the extent that recreation has stress-reduction value, the chapters are written to enrich your skill set. However, Equine-imity adds another dimension to traditional horsemanship skills by emphasizing the emotional, bioenergetic, and social aspects of each activity. For instance, before meeting a horse, we summon our Inner Smile and do some preparatory qigong postures, gestures, and breathing. We then approach each activity as a moving meditation.

So much of our educational, career, sporting, and social lives is driven by goals, competition, and success. Even some approaches to meditation foster an accomplishment mentality, which is exorcised in Tibetan Buddhist Chögyam Trungpa's *Cutting Through Spiritual Materialism.* The title says it all—a message to steer away from achievement-oriented spirituality. Somatic horsemanship is process oriented and taught in a way that honors each individual's process as unique, valid, unpressured, and unconditionally loved.

12

AND THE HORSE YOU RODE IN ON

Four Principles of Natural Horsemanship

Seth, a nurse in one of Stanford's cancer clinics, arrives a few minutes early on a warm, sunny April day for his third Equine-imity session. The ranch is idyllic—we're enjoying a few days between mud season and dust season, and we're still a good month away from fly season. Yesterday's light rain tamped down the surfaces of the trails, roads, and arenas. The enormous old oak above my little outdoor oficinita, as our Mexican ranch foreman calls it, is fully leafed out, shading our garden sitting area. To the background music of chirping birds, cooing birds, cawing birds, and the rat-a-tat-tat of two red-headed woodpeckers is added the high-up honking of Canada geese.

In his previous sessions of herd observation and grooming, Seth showed a high degree of awareness of his own body and those of the horses and their surroundings. He noted their ear and tail movements, noticed when they noticed him from afar, noticed when Bandit, the young overo paint, sidled up to him a little closer for more massaging. I imagined Seth to be a most caring, perceptive nurse. So for this advanced practice visit, I invite him to play with my horse Serena in the round pen, where he can more deeply experience the give and take of communication using a natural horsemanship model. This model will inform all the activities described in the next four chapters.

What Is Natural Horsemanship?

> *When people think of natural horsemanship, that could mean a lot of things. It isn't natural for a horse to be around people, and it's not natural for a person to be sitting on him either. When we use these words, we speak about what's natural for the horse to do within his own boundaries.*

—Bill Dorrance

Natural horsemanship has come to mean a humane, post *Ben-Hur* way of working with horses.[1] It arose in reaction to harsh methods used by cowboys in Mexico and the American West in the 1800s and early 1900s. In those times, as now, feral horses roamed the land in great numbers, free for the taking. Cowboys trapped them, roped them, and took a no-nonsense, utilitarian approach to quickly "breaking" them for ranch work. They used whips and chains, laid them down with hog-tied legs, and tethered them to snubbing posts, withholding food and water. These methods were meant to force the horse into speedy submission and show him who was boss for the jobs ahead. Often these techniques resulted in a horse with a broken spirit or an outlaw horse who could not be tamed, became dangerous, and had to be returned to the wild or slaughtered. To the extent that any type of coercive—some would say abusive—practices persist

---

1   The 1925 production of *Ben-Hur* was one of the worst animal cruelty disasters in Hollywood history. More than 150 horses died on the set.

today, they are based on the trainer's need to dominate the horse through fear and pain.

More compassionate models of gentling—"starting"— horses have been documented since Xenophon's manual in Greece in 350 BCE. In the mid-to late twentieth century, the evolution of various schools of natural horsemanship became associated with three generations of trainers: first Tom and Bill Dorrance; then Ray Hunt; and more recently, Mark Rashid and Pat Parelli.[2] Some NH clinicians have created self-branded equipment to facilitate a repertoire of structured techniques they introduce in a prescribed sequence, especially to young green horses and old green people.

Four training principles are common to most schools of natural horsemanship:

1. **Pressure and release (negative reinforcement).**[3] In the horse communication world, any time we make a request of a horse we are exerting pressure. Sometimes just entering the horse's personal bubble, a diameter that varies from horse to horse, and requesting that she share her space, is a form of pressure. Especially for moves as familiar and low key as coming up to touch

---

2   The list of those whom I respect from personal experience also includes, in alphabetical order, Buck Brannaman, Karen Parelli Hagen, Chris Irwin, John Lyons, Crissi McDonald, Lyn Ringrose-Moe (Cowboy Dressage), Sylvia Scott, and Jerry Tindell (horses and mules).

3   "Negative" in the terminology of operant conditioning means something is *taken away*. It does not mean unpleasant. "Reinforcement" means the behavior is encouraged. A common misconception about operant conditioning is that negative reinforcement means a noxious stimulus is administered. However, introducing something disagreeable is *positive de-enforcement,* or punishment.

her or asking her to walk with us, the pressure of a request is not necessarily stressful. The release of pressure is the reward we give immediately upon noticing that the horse is complying with our request. The horse learns from the release, which creates relaxation, not from the pressure, which may create resistance. Sometimes the release we provide is just the act of stepping back and withdrawing our ch'i, as in Seth's longeing lesson below.

2. **Gradual escalation of request pressure.** Sylvia Scott teaches the "V"olume principle of starting with the quietest way of making a request and then, if needed, gradually getting louder. At the soft and narrow end of the V is the mere thought of what we wish the horse to do, a visual image that we transmit. If she doesn't read our minds, we move up the V, adding nonverbal body language such as shifting our weight. If needed, we further increase the volume with a word or a sound. Maximum volume is reached with a material aid like the lead rope or a "magic wand"—the riding whip. After a while, the horse learns the progression and responds to the softer cues, sometimes down to just a mental suggestion. The key to moving up the V is to keep our emotions at a whisper. Turning up the volume of signals should not mean escalating frustration, impatience, or anger.

3. **Baby steps, stepping back.** Requests must sometimes be broken down into smaller tasks until the horse can accomplish each tiny step in the sequence. You must watch carefully for signs of misunderstanding or fear, like snorting or showing the whites of the eyes. If you reach the point where the horse is confused or afraid,

go back to the last step that she understood and was comfortable with, even if it's just standing still. A horse cannot learn a new task in a place of distress.

For instance, if you're asking your horse to cross over a pole on the ground, she might initially refuse and pull back. That pole might be a snake! You will need to take her back to where she last felt safe, let her assess the situation, and repeat the approach. With one or many tries, she will get a step closer each time, and eventually—over minutes, hours, or days—step over the pole.

Some horses might be perplexed by the dan tien press, even more so by the dan tien hug. Neither is in their natural repertoire. If your horse doesn't agree to these gestures, however slowly and gently you attempt them, you will have to break them down into more familiar forms of touching. If at any time your horse looks worried or moves away, go back to the last thing she accepted and try again. You may not get all the way to the press or hug the first day, and that is just fine with her.

4. **Rewarding the tiny try (positive reinforcement).**[4] We reward the smallest try by giving words of praise, a stroke on the neck, or even a piece of carrot. The smallest try might manifest as a softening of the eyes, a brief look in your direction, or lifting a hoof toward the requested end. In the pressure-release sequence, the release must be given at the first sign of the try. Timing is everything. A caveat among equine behaviorists is

---

4 "Positive" means *adding* something. Positive reinforcement is adding something to encourage a behavior. "Positive" does not mean "nice," but for *reinforcement*, it is something pleasant. *Positive de-enforcement* is adding a deterrent, a punishment.

that we have three seconds in which the horse will associate something he did with our response to it. If you give him the release or the carrot ten seconds after he correctly responds to your request, he will not see the cause-and-effect relationship.

Opinions vary on whether and when to give a horse food treats. My practice is to offer treats only at specific times during training and tacking up. I never treat immediately upon greeting my, or any, horse. Treats will not make a horse love you and will often make him pushy. Because of the subtle and honest interactions we encourage in Equine-imity, I recommend against creating relationships based on your being the Carrot Lady. Most horses are tuned in to the words and tone of praise. A warm, cheery "Goo' boy" or "Goo' girl" can be as welcome as an apple.

Equine-imity does not try to make you into a horse trainer. However, every interaction we have with a horse is a form of training. Deep within the evolutionary makeup of prey animals is the instinct that learning and remembering can mean life or death. The training is reciprocal as we discover eachother's ways. This mutual coaching is based on the heightened awareness of eachother's actions and reactions. The horse comes by his from birth. You are honing your sensitivity with the introductory qigong exercises and the Wu Duan Jin forms. In preparing you for safe and trusting partnerships with horses, we present natural horsemanship as an approach to a unique relationship, not a set of rules or techniques.

Approach to Relationship—Softness and Feel

In his book *Journey to Softness: In Search of Feel and Connection with the Horse,* Mark Rashid defines softness as a quality that starts from the inside with our emotions and affects all our physical actions. Not to be mistaken for passivity, softness is more than just a pantomime of surface gentleness. We must be soft and peaceful within in order for the horse to sense gentleness without. Requests we make of the horse can be resolute and decisive while still coming from a place of softness. In qigong, as in Rashid's black belt practice of aikido, softness begins with the grounding and centering of the wu ji posture and dan tien breathing. Paradoxically, internal softness enables us to relate to horses with the firmness, fairness, and consistency they require. We cannot be soft just when we come to the barn, while going about the rest of our lives in a hard-hearted way. We must seek to live more softly in all we do, even in actions that are outwardly assertive or physically forceful.

Rashid's prescription for softness derives from the elusive notion of *feel* as indescribably described by Bill Dorrance in *True Horsemanship Through Feel. Feel* is not just in the hands, as is usually meant in reference to bit pressure on the horse's mouth. It is a total body quality that permeates both the physical, sensory connection and the emotional connection. We develop these connections as we tune in to increasingly more subtle nuances of communication. In a sense, *feel* is something that cannot be taught except by the horses themselves. If there is resistance, fear, or confusion, we must seek a more adept way to give and get the *feel.* Cowboy Dressage pioneers Eitan and Debbie Beth-Halachmy are philosophical heirs to Bill Dorrance and Ray Hunt. They say that the distinguishing feature of feel is its two-way nature: any handler can send a soft message to a horse, but true partnership can only happen when we feel the horse sending soft messages back.

Zen Mind, Beginner's Mind

Sometimes experienced horse people have a harder time adapting to natural horsemanship than beginners with no previous indoctrination.

Before Equine-imity, our most popular Stanford equine-guided education (EGE) course was Medicine and Horsemanship. Designed for medical students, with versions for physicians, nurses, and other healthcare providers, Medicine and Horsemanship teaches clinician-patient communication, teamwork, leadership, and self-care. The activities are more structured and skills oriented than Equine-imity and are metaphors for clinical scenarios like the outpatient clinic, the hospital ward, and the operating room. One of the most fun and challenging activities is UNinformed Consent, also called Haunted House. It teaches clinicians how to recognize and comfort patients who are afraid, whether of chemotherapy or a flu shot.

Before attempting Haunted House, the students study the syllabus chapter on the principles of natural horsemanship. In class, teams of three to four students try to guide their horses through a scary obstacle course of balloons and streamers leading up to a shiny, crinkly space blanket. Most horses are somewhere between tentative about and terrified of this layout.

Haunted House calls up all our principles of natural horsemanship—pressure and release; the gradually escalating request; small, slow steps from the last place of comfort; and rewarding the smallest try. The prime directive, the measure of success in the activity, is to become *aware* of when your horse-patient exhibits fear. The goal of getting the horse past the balloons and over the space blanket is secondary. Not infrequently, students with previous horse experience attempt to "succeed" by using the dominance model they were schooled in.

Haunted House, March 2017. We have nine students in teams of three with three horses in a 60-meter round ring. March has come in like a lion, blowing the space blanket and balloons in a way that looks especially dire to a horse. Initially, the horses are at the back of the arena in their comfort zone—the "waiting room." The students take turns, one team at a time, in leading their horses to the "operating room." They are meant to be alert for early signs of fear, before any outright panic sets in.[5]

One of our second-year medical students is a tall, leggy, athletic gal named Jan. She is wearing black Ariat boots and Kerrits leggings, sure signs of a horsey person. In fact, Jan had been an upper-level dressage rider as an undergrad. Like many equestrians in competitive disciplines, she had been coached in the tradition that the human must be the boss, directing every step, and the horse must follow orders. This convention is especially true in dressage, an exacting, high-precision dance of horse and rider. Jan is the leader of Team Pippin, using the rope to urge this cute and spooky little bay Arabian to the haunted house. Her right hand clutches the rope near the clip attached to the halter. The Micromanagement Hold. Her left hand is in a fist a little way down the rope. As the team gets closer to the writhing balloons, Jan is heedless of Pippin's snorting,

5   Desensitizing horses to scary objects is called *sacking out,* as in the old days when it was done by flapping a burlap sack. Sacking out helps horses become less fearful, less stressed, and safer to be with, especially when riding.

pulling back, and showing the whites of his eyes. It's not that she doesn't notice. It's that the more he resists, the harder she pulls on him. As her teammates become increasingly disconcerted, and before Pippin might rear up with Jan attached to him, we facilitators call a Time Out. In EGE, facilitators generally refrain from barging in with our own observations and interpretations. The nature of experiential learning is for participants to reach realizations on their own.[6] In a Time Out, usually called for safety concerns, we first ascertain the participant's awareness of what was going on when we stopped the clock.

I ask Jan, "How is it going for you?"

Jan explains, "Pippin is being disobedient and not respecting me." I say nothing.

We invite her team members, all new to horses, to share what each of them had observed and how each is feeling. With their Zen beginners' minds, they describe Pippin's behaviors and remind Jan and eachother that the prime directive was to notice how stressed and fearful he had become. They suggest that he needed to go back to his place of comfort and learning, possibly all the way to the waiting room.

Being with horses is not a contest we have to win. It is also not an exercise in anthropomorphizing human concepts of obedience and respect in ways that horses do not conceive of, much less act out. Pippin was not cognitively forming the notion, much less intending, "disrespect." (We will have more to say about respect in chapter 16.)

---

6   Medicine and Horsemanship and to a lesser extent, Equine-imity, uses the EAGALA SPUD'S model of equine-assisted learning. www.eagala.org

After the other students have left, Jan remains. She is rueful with the realization that her coercion of Pippin is from her old habits of horsemanship, missing the metaphor of compassion for the patient. Group hug, Jan and facilitators.

If there's one thing that's more gratifying than teaching beginners, it's having someone with ingrained patterns of horsemanship consider that there might be another way. With all that has been written, YouTubed, taught in clinics, and proselytized at our 300-person, 300-opinion ranch, we have myriad conflicting theories and styles of horsemanship. There is no one completely correct Daoist or other Way. I must humbly remind myself to approach with a beginner's mind each new horse I meet and each meeting with my own horse.

The Round Pen—the Crucible of Relationship

Seth and I leave mi oficinita, *collect Serena, and walk to a round arena in a private part of the ranch. Once in the round ring, Serena sniffs along the ground like a bloodhound, finds her spot, paws the dirt, and goes down front legs first to lie on her side. She has an exuberant roll, left to right, right to left, waving her legs in the air, wriggling on her back. Then she lies still in bliss for a few seconds, stands up, and shakes off the sand like a wet poodle.*

This is the prelude to free longeing ("lunj-ing") with a short riding whip, which we term a wand. It does not come into contact with the horse, but is an extension of our arms in transmitting ch'i.

In line longeing, a 30-foot rope of webbed cotton is attached to the horse's halter. The person stands in the center of the ring, with a direct physical connection and partial physical control, and asks the horse to move in a circle around her. She also typically uses a 6-foot-long wand with a 6-foot-long cotton whip at its end to signal or nudge—never beat—her horse. Because I have some mild residual vertigo symptoms from years ago, I cannot keep rotating in circles at the end of the line. Fortunately, I have always preferred free longeing. In free longeing, the horse and human are connected by body language, ch'i, and the sixth sense.

Serena and I walk the perimeter together in both directions without a lead rope. Then we do the same at a trot. As I can't canter as fast as Serena, I withdraw to the center of the circle and ask her for the three gaits from there.

Suddenly April regresses to March and a strong wind blows across the arena. Serena is less serene. Energized by the wind ch'i, she surges into bucking and running in a full-out gallop. Once she has had her way, we resynchronize our bodies. We go into the wu ji. I hold my arm down and out at a 45-degree angle and point to the ground, the request for walk. My arm parallel to the ground asks for trot. Arm held up and out at a 45-degree angle to the sky means canter. Not just my arm position, but how fast I move my body, how much ch'i I exude, and how I move in toward her and withdraw away from her choreographs our dance. The withdrawal phase is key, given principle #1 of natural horsemanship: releasing pressure.

Serena's and my signaling system doesn't immediately translate to a new person. We communicate on unique personal levels. Seth moves into Serena's bubble a little too quickly for the walk request. He holds the wand too high, almost threatening. The excess energy sends Serena off at a fast trot. We retreat back to the center of the ring, make our bodies small, almost crouching, and Serena halts, facing us. Even when Seth exactly mimics my arm positions, Serena chooses her own gaits. Clearly she senses energy as well as body language. Over the next fifteen minutes, Seth develops extraordinary finesse, timing, and awareness of his and Serena's blended ch'i. Serena responds with a calm progression through the gaits, coming to a gentle stop when Seth drops the wand and kneels, eyes lowered, Little Sally Walker style, in the middle of the ring. He has learned a powerful lesson in whole-body ch'i pressure, blending, and release.

In the activities described in the next four chapters, you will apply the principles of natural horsemanship, subject to your mentor's instructions. If you are already experienced with horses, Equine-imity might offer you some new approaches and activities with which to mentor yourself. When in doubt, don't read the book; read the horse.

> *There is no such thing as a horse whisperer. There never has been and never will be. The idea is an affront to the horse. You can talk and listen to horses all you want, and what you will learn, if you pay close attention, is that they live on open ground way beyond language and that language, no matter how you characterize it, is a poor trope for what horses understand about themselves and about humans. You need to practice only three things, patience, observation and humility.*
> — Verlyn Klinkenborg, obituary for Bill Dorrance, *New York Times*, July 24, 1999

13

PHASE 1: *CON SU PERMISO*

Meet and Greet, Safety, Dan Tien Intimacies

*I*t was the first day of an eight-week equine-assisted psychotherapy
(EAP) program for at-risk middle school girls in Northern
California. Each week, the girls had one group therapy session
and one individual session. For Andie's private session, Denise
Holliday, doctor of clinical psychology and EAP practitioner, led
her fifteen-year-old client into a grassy pasture with a herd of six
mares and geldings. The horses were grazing, each one uniformly
calm and focused. Andie, a troubled teen in the shared custody
of divorced, alcoholic parents, was invited to meet and greet each
horse one by one. She slowly went around to three horses, touching
and stroking them. When she came to the fourth horse, Penny, a
beautiful copper-colored chestnut mare, Andie began to cry. Dr.
Holliday was mystified.

Andie explained, "I just feel like this horse is really sad."
Unknown to Andie, Penny had recently miscarried a foal. Unknown
to Dr. Hall, Andie had a secret she had told no one: two months
before, she'd had an abortion.

Dr. Hall told me, "Andie felt a kinship with this horse right
away. I was just blown away by it."

First Contact

Meeting a horse is an awesome experience, sometimes full of surprises and unexpected connections. Whether it's your first horse or your hundredth, that initial contact is like Michelangelo's painting in the Sistine Chapel, with its magic arc of ch'i between the fingers of God and Adam.

When relating to horses in Equine-imity, we need no agenda. We can be content just to hang out and observe the herd. There is nothing we have to accomplish, nothing the horses expect us to do to earn an A+. Awareness and energy are exchanged whether or not we are in physical contact.

All cultures and species have rituals for meeting and greeting. Westerners shake hands. In Asian cultures, bowing is customary. Animals, too, have characteristic ways of making introductions. Dogs sniff under eachother's tails. Cats perform several rounds of staring, blinking, and looking away. Chickens squawk and flutter and poke to establish, literally, a pecking order. Horses introduce themselves by blowing and sniffing at eachother's nostrils and signaling with their ears, head carriage, rumps, and hind legs whether their intentions are honorable.

The first step in connecting with a horse is observation. Watch the horse from a distance at which she doesn't yet respond to your presence. Notice how she makes you feel somatically and emotionally. A horse dozing or grazing can give you a sense of peace. A horse rolling, running, or bucking can infuse you with her exuberance and abandon.

As you get nearer to the horse, notice if and when he seems to notice you. As we learned from Dream in chapter 10, horses know we're there, even if they give no visible indicator of their awareness. Bask in the horse's nonjudgmental mindfulness. He will notice everything and criticize nothing. I am always amazed and amused at how horses recognize their person's car, heard but not seen, from half a mile down the road. They will start pacing and whinnying long before I see their person come around the corner.

It's the nature of horses to be sociable and curious, wanting to check out new objects and people. However, coming into a horse's space, and letting him into yours, is a gradual process of feeling out eachother's willingness to relate. *Con su permiso* means *with your permission* in Spanish and denotes mutual consent. I learned the con su permiso approach from my first equine-guided learning mentor, Barbara Rector. We ask the horse for approval to come into his space, his bubble. We ask ourselves if we are okay admitting the horse into our bubble, especially if he initiates the move. We must be alert for any sign that the answer might be no. From the horse, pinning his ears, moving away, or flashing his haunches; from our own bodies, tightness, breath holding, or butterflies in the stomach—all are indicators from one or both parties that we might need to be content, for the time being, to watch and wait from a place of comfort.

Notions of personal space vary among individuals and are in part culturally and familially determined. In some cultures, strangers embrace with bear hugs and cheekside kisses. In other cultures, even spouses don't touch in public. Horses, too, have individualized preferences about personal space and ritual for first contact. Greeting behaviors may differ around different parts of their bodies, such as with head-shy horses, and may differ from day to day and season to season.

You might feel both afraid of horses and magically drawn

to them. You should only interact with them when you and they feel comfortable with each level of observation, approach, and contact.

Once physical contact is accepted on both sides, it might be possible to proceed to the dan tien press and the dan tien hug or simply to a sensual exploration of mutually satisfying petting, massaging, and grooming.

Your mentor will guide you in the social niceties her horse expects.

Safety and Etiquette

Here are some general guidelines that will help you feel safe, confident, and polite around horses.

- Wear sturdy, closed-toe-and-heel footwear. Sneakers, running shoes, and hiking or riding boots are appropriate. Inappropriate are sandals, clogs, slingbacks, and flimsy or high-heeled fashion shoes. Horses do not have an accurate sense of where they plant their feet in relation to you. If a horse inadvertently steps on you, you do not want to be in flip-flops.
- Horses appreciate a relaxed, deliberate approach to their visual and auditory fields. They do not like to be taken by surprise, especially in the blind spot around their tails. (See the visual field diagram in chapter 1.) They might spook at unfamiliar objects and noises. Let your horse know where you're coming from, where you are, and where you're going on and around her body. Use a gentle but firm touch and a soft voice.
- Some horses seem to be sensitive to the buzz we give off after too much caffeine. One Internet blogger said,

"I had to give up my double-shot mochas because all the horses ran away from me."

- If you are moved to greet using hand-to-muzzle contact, do so with the back of your hand, not the palm. A palm-up greeting means "I have food" or "I *am* food." This is a tease at best and, at worst, can result in nipped fingers. Horses do not make friends like dogs who sniff and lick your hand. Avoid prolonged or repeated contacts with the horse's mouth. Move instead to connect with her neck, shoulder, or back as demonstrated by your mentor.

Once you have given *su permiso* for initial physical contact, you may continue the introduction by gently but firmly stroking your horse along the large muscles. More on massaging horses in the next chapter.

The Myth of the Crab Walk

Some instructions say to approach a horse only at her shoulder. Possibly one purpose of this advice is to trick a hard-to-catch horse into thinking we're not out to halter her. But a horse who doesn't want to get caught will not be fooled for as long as it takes to bring the halter out from behind our backs. She will get away no matter what the subterfuge. Usually this rule is meant to caution you from popping up unannounced in the horse's frontal blind spot. However, as we saw in the visual field diagram, there is no blind spot in front of the horse's face. When horses walk to eachother and to us, they don't skitter up sideways like crabs on a beach. They come head-on, as we can naturally and politely do with them.

A Word About Treats

Most horses are inveterate chow hounds. Highly food driven, they would rather eat than do almost anything else. In the wild and in pasture, they graze off and on throughout the day. This grazing is not necessarily eating, but often just an oral fixation meditation. Human-introduced temptations like carrots, apples, and Mrs. Pasture's cookies are irresistible.

As I mentioned in the previous chapter, in Equine-imity we do not hand feed. For one thing, we do not want to encourage pushy, treat-seeking behavior toward our participants. We do not want a horse, much less a herd of horses, to charge up thinking, *There's an Equine-imity person! Let's see what she brought me!* Mainly, we want to foster clean, honest relationships based on balanced exchanges of energy, not based on our need to feed. If a participant brings treats, they are placed in pans for one horse by himself or for a few horses in an arena for a class. We never treat while among the herd.

The Dan Tien Press and the Dan Tien Hug

After the introductory petting, the next level of contact is optionally the dan tien hug and the dan tien press. These gestures are meant to provide additional minimum-agenda intimacies that are mutually pleasurable to horse and human.

The press and hug are techniques derived from aikido partner *kata* and tai ji Push Hands. *Aikido* means *the Way of joining energy.* (*Ai* is blending; *ki* is ch'i; *do* is Dao, the Way.) Blending our energy centers with the horse's energy centers is one of the most relaxing things we can do. Horses are heavily, literally, grounded in their connection with the earth. Equine energy healers such as acupuncturists feel that the horse's dan tien, Bubbling Springs, and Lao Gong energy centers correspond to ours. This makes it easy to imagine, then feel, that we are joining our energies with our horse during the dan tien press and dan tien hug and when mounted.

The key to both the dan tien press and the dan tien hug is to move slowly, deliberately, and confidently, letting your horse feel where you are and where you're going. In each case, you maintain the wu ji posture and dan tien breathing, centering, and grounding. If at any time the horse shows confusion or discomfort, back off and reassess. I recommend that the press and, especially, the hug be performed only when the horse is at liberty; that is, not tied. That way, he has the freedom to move away if he doesn't care for the gestures or when he's had enough.

For the dan tien press, the placement of your body should be familiar to the horse, as it is the same as for grooming and saddling. You approach the horse as usual, introducing yourself from the front. You begin by petting him on the neck. Then, maintaining contact with your hands, you move slowly down his neck until you are facing his side. Put your hands at your shoulder height, shoulder width apart. Feet are also shoulder width apart. Go into the wu ji, keeping your shoulders down, chest open, knees soft, and elbows slightly bent. Be mindful of your feet: remember that horses are generally unaware of where their feet are in relation to you. If they step on you, it's never on purpose.

Once in place, press firmly with your hands, keeping them still. Imagine the horse's ch'i rising up from the earth through the Lao Gong and Bubbling Springs centers in his feet, up through his legs, and into his dan tien under your hands. Imagine your breath and ch'i flowing from the horse's dan tien into your hands, up your arms, down through your

Dan tien press, Sasha and Lokin

dan tien, legs, and feet, and into the earth. Allow yourself as much time as you need to enjoy this relaxed, grounded state. If your horse is grazing while you're in contact and moves to another patch of grass, you can follow him in the press position. (Just be sure he is not purposely moving away from you.) Following along is a truly unique form of moving meditation!

Silver

For my fifty-fourth birthday, Ruben and I spent a weekend at the Costanoa Resort on Coastal Highway 1 near Pescadero. The resort had a trail riding outfit with fourteen mostly rescued, mostly Tennessee Walking Horses. There up on the mesa, with a stiff ocean breeze blowing across the corral, I met Silver, a true white, with pink skin. Silver was and remained one of the nicest horses I've ever known. (Many years later, I would lease him from his person at Webb Ranch.) At Blue Sky Riding, Silver was the gentlest horse in the dude string, the go-to guy for children and beginner adults. He was as near bomb-proof as a horse can be. One of the trail guides would park her two-year-old baby on him while she tacked up the other horses. Silver stood stock still in his role as nanny.

In 2012, after years of faithfully — and safely — carrying dudes from all over the world through hills, beaches, and forests, Silver retired to horse heaven-on-earth, Front Pasture of Webb Ranch. There, he was our star Equine-imity horse, especially because he didn't mind being taken away from the herd to play with our participants. One participant, a cancer patient, DeeDee, came many times during the course of her illness just for Silver. At the beginning, she could make it up the hill to him. As time went on, I brought him to where she could walk to him on the flats. Two weeks before she crossed over, DeeDee said goodbye to Silver from her wheelchair in the parking lot. He had been her comfort and salvation for almost three years.

Silver was relaxed and happy in the pasture. However, he had one disconcerting habit: he was a head-tosser. Some days he would shake his head up and down continuously and violently for no apparent reason. Flies, chiropractic malalignment, and dental issues had been eliminated as causes.

Most likely, the years in the dude string, with hundreds of tourists jerking on his reins, caused Silver's behavior. Do you remember from chapter 12 that two key principles in natural horsemanship are 1) immediately rewarding the smallest try and 2) using release of pressure as the reward? The most common use of pressure and release is when asking a horse to whoa. Most horses, especially at the end of the trail, will stop with very little force. They are happy to be home. As soon as their feet slow down, you relax the reins. However, novice riders yank abruptly and forcefully and keep pulling on the horse's mouth even after his feet have stopped. Not rewarding the try, not offering the release. The horse will seek to relieve the pressure of the bit in his mouth by grabbing back the reins with a vehement shake of his head. With Silver, it seemed that the rein-grabbing, bit-relieving gesture had become a chronic tic.

One of my earliest clients to try the dan tien press was Harriet, a psychotherapist who is also a Reiki practitioner. On the day Harriet came to Front Pasture, the herd was lolling in the shade of the oak copse along the main road. Silver, inclined to be a loner, was standing by himself up a little incline in a bed of withered pin oak leaves. This was one of his random head-shaking days. Even with his head pumping up and down vigorously, Silver was otherwise calm and happy to engage in meet and greet. For the dan tien press, Harriet put her hands on his sides, grounded herself in her belly breathing, and "ran her energy" as she did for Reiki. After about 10 seconds, Silver stopped tossing his head! Harriet kept her position for more than 5 minutes, during which time Silver's head stayed low and quiet. From then on, I was often able to use the dan tien press to tranquilize Silver's head tossing.

The dan tien hug is one of the ultimate acts of horse-human intimacy. You will be body-to-body, feeling eachother breathe. However, if your horse can't relate it to something he already knows, the hug might seem weirder than the press. Therefore, to position yourself for the hug, it's important to move from the familiar to what might be new. Spend some time petting your horse's neck. Move down the neck slowly, keeping

Dan tien hug, author and Rhett

your hands on him. Your destination is the place shown in the photo, just behind the horse's shoulder.

Stand sideways, facing the horse's head. Drape your inside arm—in this photo, the left arm—over her back, heavy and relaxed. A healthy horse can carry 15 to 20 percent of her weight on her back, so your 10- to 20-pound arm will not be burdensome to her. Keep your outside hand—the right in the photo—on the horse's shoulder or down by your side. Tuck the convexity (outside bulge) of the horse's body, called the barrel, into the concave curve of your waist and hip. Make a firm seal. Drop into the wu ji and begin your dan tien breathing. If your horse is still with her head raised, you will be able to feel her barrel expand into the curve of your body with each of her breaths. (If she is grazing, it will be harder to feel her breathing.)

I fondly remember my longest dan tien hug. It was in Front Pasture, with Silver's friend Mikey, a huge Belgian draft-mustang cross palomino. We stood among the herd in the sun-speckled woods, Mikey dozing, hugging for twenty minutes.

The breath and energy flow in the dan tien hug and the dan tien press is a continuous cycle. Visualizing it in one direction, the ch'i comes up through the earth, up through your horse's legs and body, into your body, down your legs, and back into the earth. You can also visualize the circulation in the other direction, starting from the earth, up through your legs and body, through your horse, and back down into the earth. The circulation of horse-human ch'i is even more tangible during the meditation ride, where the Microcosmic Orbit qigong meditation comes into play.

Part with Heart

Although our departures matter little to most horses, I make a ritual of leave taking for my own satisfaction. A pet. Or a bow. Or a gesture of Gassho. Or a verbal goodbye and thank you. Or all of the above with the Inner Smile. Whatever, in that moment, expresses appreciation and closure. My horse might already be head down in hay or off to rejoin his buddies. But at least I've done my part with heart.

14

PHASE 2: OMMMMMM GROOMING

The 6 Ms of Touching Horses

*I*n the TV series *Mad Men*, set in 1962, Betty Draper is an up-Hudson ad executive's wife who plays homemaker while her husband works in the City and plays with other women. Resuming the riding lessons from her teenage years is her Mother's Little Helper to ease the pain of a marriage on the rocks. Betty's riding habit is a natty plaid wool jacket, starched white shirt with ratcatcher collar, jodhpurs with ballooning thighs, and shiny black knee-high boots. Thus attired, Betty steps up on the mounting block. To further her ritual immunity to any speck of dirt, the stable boy hands Betty a clean, lustrous, saddled horse.

For aristocratic riders, and those turned out in finery for horse shows, a hired groom or your Show Mom still performs this service. Often, in both high-level competitions and beginner-level lessons, this handoff of the horse-as-vehicle can be as impersonal as getting your car from valet parking. However, most equestrians groom their own horses, at least enough to get them clean before saddling up. But grooming is not merely a practical step in preparation for riding. It is a rich, relaxing activity in itself.

Horses perform mutual "grooming"—at least that's how we anthropomorphize the behavior of the horses in the photo. We see them alongside one another, massaging eachother with their lips and scraping eachother's shoulders, backs, and haunches with their teeth. The telltale grass stain on a white horse's shoulders is a sure sign that she's been necking with a buddy. Most horses enjoy being groomed by humans in a like manner and will present specific body parts for attention.

Horses grooming eachother

The 6 Ms of Grooming

Once your horse has been properly greeted as described in the previous chapter, you are ready to groom. (Even a horse you've seen every day for years should have the courtesy of the greeting ritual before grooming.) You can remember all aspects of grooming a horse by thinking of the word *om*, a Sanskrit syllable used as a soft, droning chant for meditation. Ommmmmm with six Ms is a mnemonic for the six reasons to groom. The 6 Ms of grooming are presented here in an order that goes from the mundane to the metaphysical.

Mechanical: cleaning the horse, especially for riding. A horse should not suffer dirt, burrs, or pebbles on his back or in his tail, mane, or feet. If you have ever had dust under your contact lens or a foxtail in your sock, you know how annoying such a small thing can be. A horse who has something under his blanket, lodged in his sole, or stuck in his tail will not only be uncomfortable but may rear, buck, or trip and be dangerous to ride. "Having a burr under your blanket" is cowboy talk for being in a surly mood. Mud left on the coat and in the hooves promotes bacterial and fungal infections. Mucous around the eyes attracts annoying, sometimes disease-carrying, flies. Eyes should be gently wiped with a damp lint-free cloth.

Cleaning the feet is an important part of grooming. Neglected feet may harbor sharp objects that lead to abscesses and will be prone to infections, especially when the ground is wet.

Medical: health and injury assessment. During grooming, we go over every part of the horse's body, inspecting for cuts, bites, infections, lumps, and swollen joints. We are alert for areas where the horse may resist being groomed, a possible indicator of soreness.

Some horses object to being touched around the face or parts of it, such as mouth, eyes, and ears. These head-shy horses become that way through an inborn sense of self-protection or through having been mishandled around the face with slapping, harsh grooming, rough bridling, or painful bits. Horses are naturally wary of sudden movements and objects above and around their heads. A horse who becomes newly head-shy may have dental issues or be ill or injured.

Mood Assessment: the overall vibe you get. Horses' moods are as changeable as ours. Referring to the variability of a horse's moods, we have a saying: "You never know what horse you're riding today." Horses are sensitive to changes in the weather and to smells and sounds that are beneath our perception thresholds. On a windy day, horses are noticeably more alert and frisky. Wind creates new sounds and carries more smells. Mares in estrus ("heat") might behave in surprising ways to show they're in the mood. We can tell whether a horse is perky, sleepy, cranky, mellow, anxious, silly, or sad-seeming by how she responds to grooming. (We also need to be mindful of projections of our own moods and needs onto our horses.) Physical discomforts that the horse cannot put into words can show up as mood changes or as reactions to specific grooming motions. A horse can assess your frame of mind too. If your relationship is ongoing, you might notice her reacting differently to your different moods.

One of the best indicators of mood, as well as where her attention is, is her ears. Ears on a relaxed, happy horse are upright or slightly flopped to the sides. A horse who pins her ears backward is in a bad mood, in pain, cranky by nature, or signaling she does not wish to be handled in the way you are doing it. If a horse pins her ears, stop what you're doing and reassess the situation with your mentor and with the horse herself. Proceed slowly and mindfully.

Manners: cooperation and boundaries. A horse's ground and riding manners are a function of her personality, training, health, and mood. Especially when you encounter a new horse, grooming is one of the best ways to assess her barnside manner. Does she stand quietly for each step in the process? Does she lift all four feet when asked or even in anticipation of being asked? Does she come into your space aggressively, nosing your body for treats or trying to nip your hands and clothing? Is she in the habit of pinning her ears back and making a nasty face whenever she's approached? A previously well-mannered horse may express physical or emotional discomfort by forgetting her manners. Many of us humans regress into a nearly juvenile state of crankiness when we're sick. As a beginner, you should work only with well-mannered horses. Those with ongoing behavioral issues that manifest as unpleasantries during grooming are not appropriate for Equine-imity 101.

Melding: horse-human bonding. Grooming is the ideal time to make a sweet, intimate connection with your horse. With practice and a spirit of exploration, you will find her favorite spots for currying, brushing, scratching, and massaging. Grooming builds mutual trust and comfort. This is a good time to try the dan tien press and, if the horse isn't tied, the dan tien hug.

In melding, you are asking the horse to participate with you in the experience.

Meditation: me time. Unlike melding, the grooming "me"ditation is an internally directed process for your own physical, emotional, and psychospiritual benefit. Go ahead and feel a little selfish as you focus on your own enjoyment.

Grooming a horse is one of the most relaxing activities we can undertake. The Inner Smile can't help but come out. Brushing the mane and tail, which, unlike our hair, have no pain sensation, can be profoundly meditative.

In Equine-imity, we concentrate on the Ms of Melding and Meditation during all the activities.

Time Is Love

Grooming is a lesson in being on horse time. Like everything else we do around horses, grooming should never be rushed or cursory. Many lifelong equestrians dwell mostly on the first two Ms. When riding is squeezed in between a full-time job and making the family dinner, there might be no time for the finer Ms in life. But done mindfully, unhurriedly, and with sensitivity, grooming is quality time for horse and human. In *Zen Mind, Zen Horse*, Allan Hamilton, MD, compares grooming to the ritual of a tea ceremony.

> The purpose of ritual is to transpose our thinking from the physical to the symbolic. It allows the participant to experience a metaphor. The imposition of ritual transforms any task, no matter how mundane, into an exercise in spiritual awareness.

For what tasks in your life is grooming a metaphor? Can you think of three activities or tasks that you can perform more joyfully and with spiritual awareness by making them into rituals? (Think washing dishes, creating a spreadsheet, making a difficult phone call.)

15

The M.O. of the OM

Tying, Tools, and Tips

Question: How many horse experts does it take
to change a light bulb?
Answer: 100. One to change the bulb, 99 to say
"That's not the way I do it."

*L*ike the options for lassoing cattle—taking a dally vs.
tying on—the modi operandi suggested in this chapter
are not meant to be hard and fast. As I noted previously,
there is no one correct way to do anything with horses. Most
horse people are highly opinionated, and there is considerable
disagreement about the best way to halter, lead, tie, tack up,
train, and ride. What is never wrong from the horse's point
of view is softness, kindness, clarity, and consistency. Horses
appreciate routine and predictability, especially when a new
person—you!—comes on the scene. So, at least initially, you
will follow what your mentor tells you is favored by her horse.
You will find excellent additional information in the manuals
from the US Pony Club and the Certified Horsemanship
Association.

Freedom's Just Another Word for Nothing Left to Tie

Although many horses can be groomed while standing loose in a paddock or stall, pastured horses and horses for beginner grooming are best Ommmmmmed while hitched to a fixed structure. Your mentor, and the above-mentioned manuals, will teach you to halter your horse and tie her in a grooming area that allows you plenty of space and disallows the horse's wandering off.

A horse has five levels of freedom—unfenced in the wild; pastured and fenced; loose in a corral or arena; loose in a stall or paddock; or tethered. The first three are usually in the company of other horses; the last two amount to solitary confinement. Freedom for a horse is defined not just in terms of the amount of space in which she finds herself. It is also a function of her options for independent movement vs. yielding to the limitations imposed by humans. Horses in any environment may be at liberty or tethered. A tethered horse is one who is tied to a stationary object such as a hitching rail or trailer or managed by someone holding her lead rope.

In feral herds, horses run free over open range. Absent Bureau of Land Management roundups, feral horses suffer no constraints from humans. For domesticated horses, pastured herds come closest to living free in nature. Horses who are kept in stalls, even with paddocks behind them, have less room to move around and less social contact but are free within those confines to decide where to be and what to do.

Tethered horses and those attached to riders, wagons, plows, or stagecoaches are captive audiences. Their somatic responses are determined by their training and by the human demands at hand. They are usually tractable and inhibited compared with how they behave at liberty. A horse who has been trotting around the yard, high on his own energy, can settle peaceably as soon as he's haltered. The halter is like a business suit, triggering a learned response to dressing for success with humans.

As a beginner, you should only groom horses who stand quietly while tied and who have no tendency to pull back dangerously on the tie rope. Grooming a tethered horse is usually the safer, more controllable option. If you attempt to groom a liberty horse who walks off, you will need to honor his choice in the matter—or tether him to a fixed point and to your agenda.

There are three common ways to tie a horse: soft, hard, and slip, each named for how the rope feels to a horse trying to break away. Horses who are trained to give to pressure at the poll (head-neck joint) and who have halters properly fitted to deliver that pressure develop a checking reflex to counter an impulse to pull back. Horses who have not learned to give to pressure, or whose learning gets overruled by panic, may injure themselves trying to cut and run.

Soft tying means attaching the horse to something that will break if he pulls back; for example, the twine from a bale of hay. This method is preferred in programs with numerous horses and numerous handlers, especially children. Even horses who aren't prone to trying to escape may suddenly do so when frightened by low-flying helicopters, a tree falling on a roof, a cyclist careening into view, or the chaos of twenty camp kids running around. (I have witnessed all of these situations, including when the Stanford medevac choppers thunder down to the helipad half a mile from the ranch.)

I dislike soft tying for three reasons: One, the tie rope gets twisted in the baling twine and cannot be quickly released. Two, once a horse learns she can break the string, she is more likely to become a habitual puller-backer. Three, if the horse breaks the tie abruptly and with excessive force, she can flip over backward and be seriously injured. I have seen this type of somersault a few times. In one case, it happened to Sierra, a beautiful black-and-white paint mare I was leasing, who had not been known to spook *or* pull back. Sierra literally snapped when a cyclist blindsided her from around the corner of the barn. She popped her baling twine, flipped hump over rump, and got "cast" with both hind legs wedged under a parked car. It took half an hour to free her up and another long while to get her over the emotional trauma and back to grazing. A horse who has broken her tie might bolt for home, endangering herself and others. A rider can be painfully ejected from her saddle if her horse panics enough to bolt along with—or from—the runaway horse.

Hard tying refers to hitching your horse to something fixed and solid. In Western movies, cowboys throw the reins around the hitching rail in front of the saloon and saunter bowlegged through the batwing doors. Nowadays, the whiskey can wait: to avoid mouth injuries, we never tie a horse by anything attached to her bit. In hard tying, we secure the lead rope to a hitching rail or to a metal ring screwed deep into a post or welded to a trailer. The stuff of campfire stories, but rarely seen, is the hard-tied horse who pulls out the hitch rail and drags it off with her, spooking and bucking the whole way. This uncommon occurrence unfolds in slower motion than the string-breaking scenario, does not result in back flips, and gives bystanders a chance to get away.

Cross tying is a method of hard tying in which there are two fixed-anchor ropes or straps attached to posts about three feet away from the sides of the horse at the level of his cheek.

The free end of each rope is bull- or scissor-snapped, to the metal side rings on the noseband of the halter. This type of restraint has the advantage of secure, higher-up, two-point fixation that eliminates a lead rope tied at the horse's chin level. However, cross ties are more confining for the horse and limit his ability to turn to see into his blind spot. Some horses cannot tolerate them.

Cross ties also make it harder for the handler to move around him 360 degrees. Even with so-called panic snaps that might or might not release from a thousand pounds of horse, there are double the number of connections that must be freed up in an emergency. Here, however, is where the horse's routine takes precedence. If he is used to cross ties, he'll probably feel most comfortable in this configuration.

Blocker tie rings, more popular in Europe than in the US, are intermediate between soft and hard ties. They allow the lead rope to partially slip through a magnetic clasp, building up pressure slowly so as not to panic the horse. Their advantages are that they pro-vide quick and easy no-knot tying and they work on both  horses who tie quietly and those who pull back. Many horses quit pulling back once they feel the slight pressure. However, after the initial resistance, blocker rings give a slight release that can train the horse to make repeated small tugs until he is free. Many Houdini horses learn this trick all too easily.

The Bank Robber's Quick Release Tie

When either hard tying or soft tying horses to anything other than a blocker ring, we use a *quick release knot*. The term is a misnomer because the rope is never actually knotted. It is looped so it can be completely undone with a single pull on the free end in case of emergency. In the quick release tie, the lead rope is crocheted into a chain of three-to-four-inch loops. Considering how many times we tie and untie our horses in the course of being with them, the quick release tie is easiest and safest.

Most so-called quick release ties start with placing the free end of the rope through the ring or twine. This configuration defeats the purpose of rapid release, as when the crocheted part is undone, you are still left with a rope that must be pulled out of the ring. I use an ultra-quick-release tie called the bank robber's knot, similar to the highwayman's hitch or a boatman's painter hitch. (I had boats growing up, not horses.) The initial loop is made by folding the rope into a half circle about 18 inches from the horse's chin. The half circle is passed through the ring or under the rail to form the letter A. Successive As are made by looping the bight from the free end of the rope through each loop above it (see photos). In this configuration, the rope can never get stuck in the ring or on the post. A single tug on the free end unravels the rope immediately and completely. Bandits can then jump on their horses and get clean away with the loot.

A good tying length lets the rope hang slack for about 18 to 24 inches between your horse's nose and the tie ring (see photo). If the rope is too long, she can step on it or get it caught in her legs, causing her to panic and pull back. Too short, and she can sprain her neck turning her head abruptly.

Bank Robber's Knot

Ground Tying

Many horses, especially those trained Western style, can be ground tied or ground hitched; they will stand like statues when the lead rope or reins are dropped on the ground. This talent is perfected by Hollywood horses, equine actors who can be cued to stand, walk, trot, canter, gallop, whoa, rear, buck, fall, run away with stagecoaches, and abide gunshots and burning barns.

Grooming Tools

In Equine-imity, we use grooming tools primarily insofar as they provide a familiar routine for the horse. If you have groomed a horse before, you may also feel more at ease, even nostalgic, using the customary equipment. It is certainly possible, and often preferable, to use just the hands, especially for Melding and Meditation.

Curry Comb

Would you like to curry favor with your new horse friend? The word comes from the use of the curry comb. With its smooth, semi-soft rubber teeth, this tool is not a comb in the usual sense. It looks more a like a rooster's comb—bluntly

serrated and pliable. In the Mechanical phase of grooming, the curry comb is used to loosen mud and dirt and raise dust off the coat to be brushed away. In the spring shedding season, the curry comb loosens and mats in its teeth large wads of hair. (Another tool, the shedding comb, with sharp metal teeth and a long handle, is used for the X-treme grooming task of helping horses off with their winter coats.) For Melding and Meditation purposes, the curry comb offers a nice massaging action that improves skin circulation and releases tension in the muscles.

1. Approach the horse *con su permiso* as described in chapter 13.
2. Slip your hand under the belt of the curry comb, palm on the oval.
3. Start from where the horse can see you. The neck or shoulder muscle is a good place to start.
4. Use firm, circular motions starting in the direction of the hairs.
5. Be sure to curry under the mane, a heavily muscled area that is often tense and often neglected in Mechanical grooming.
6. Avoid currying on bony areas, including directly on the spine, or on tendons.
7. Avoid potentially ticklish or sensitive areas such as around the genitals.
8. Be sensitive to where the horse's attention is and how she responds to you. Keep checking in with her ears. Notice whether she moves closer to you with some part of her body, a behavior called *presenting*.
9. Become aware of the sensations coming into your own body from the movements of your arms and legs, the texture of the horse's coat, the sounds she makes, how warm she is, how she smells. Horse lovers bask in the fragrance of horses, especially when the coat is wet with rain. As a form of aromatherapy, L'Air du

Horse seems to have antidepressant properties. In his memoir *One Good Horse*, Tom Groneberg writes that he likes to keep a smelly horse blanket in his car. He calls it "cowboy air freshener."

Soft Brush

The soft brush has bristles similar to a human's shoe-polishing brush. It is used to brush away the dirt, dust, and hair raised by the curry comb. Some people curry all over, then brush. I prefer to have the curry comb in one hand and the brush in the other hand and alternate curry strokes with brush strokes. You can also use the soft brush on tendons, bone, and around the face if the horse is not head-shy or otherwise objecting.

- Use short, strong, flicking motions so the dust gets flung away from the horse.
- Check in with the horse frequently to gauge her response to you.

Horses continually shed and grow hair. To our way of seeing, we recognize two coats per year, a thick furry winter coat that sheds all over us in early spring and a short glossy summer coat. In California, we see signs of winter growth in early autumn. Veterinary science attributes the growth and shedding cycle to the amount of seasonal light that reaches the horse's pineal gland. But we horse people can attest to annual adaptations that aren't explained by just the length of day. The late-September coat, which varies year to year, is a better predictor of an early or late, hard or mild winter than the *Farmer's Almanac*.

Hoof Pick

In 1751, British farrier and anatomist Jeremiah Bridges famously said, "No foot, no horse." The horse's feet are his chief means of escape, and escape is his chief means of survival. The condition of their horses' feet has also been key to the livelihood and survival of nomads, warriors, farmers, and cattle ranchers. Horses are big, heavy animals supported by disproportionately spindly legs and small feet, so injuries and diseases of the lower extremities are the primary cause of euthanizing otherwise healthy horses.

Picking out the horse's feet is a Mechanical and Medical aspect of grooming that is ideally done at least once a day and any time your horse comes home from an activity. Unlike mutual grooming and rubbing on trees to massage and scratch, hoof picking is not something you'll see horses do on their own. Professionally trimmed, unshod horses tend to have fewer hoof problems than horses with shoes, especially badly affixed ones. Poorly fitting horseshoes are not lucky for the horse. Many horses are kept barefoot for that reason. Even expertly applied shoes trap mud, manure, and foreign bodies and require human care.

As flight animals, horses are instinctively protective of their mobility. Allowing us to pick up a foot while they stand on three legs requires trust, as it renders them temporarily vulnerable. Horses vary in how they've been trained to overcome their four-on-the-floor instinct and lift their feet. Some horses pick up the nearest hoof as soon as you bend over. Other horses seem to resist every known maneuver, especially with a stranger. It is not so much that they don't trust you; it's that you are not yet keyed in to eachother's cues. Your mentor is the best one to teach you what her horse expects. Don't try to forcibly lift the foot. You may strain yourself in doing so, and it will create resistance, rather than softness, in your horse.

Hoof picking is not a core competency—if there are indeed any—of somatic horsemanship. For a beginner, it can be a frustrating, trial-and-error process that is not especially conducive to Melding and Meditation (though satisfying if you like challenges). It is also a procedure in which you may get your hands dirty with anything your horse has stepped in. As hoof picking entails bending over and supporting a heavy leg, it might be better omitted if you have limitations in your joints or back muscles, or if you are prone to dizziness or poor balance.

The feet can be addressed in almost any order, but some horses put their foot down when it comes to their druthers. For years I went from front to back on both sides. Then I met a horse who would not lift her right front until I did her right rear in a continuous counterclockwise direction. So by the convention that every horse since has accepted, I now go left front, left rear, right rear, right front.

To maximize the chance of getting your horse to give you her hoof, using the example of the left front leg:

1. Stand with your left side at your horse's left front leg and face his rear, parallel to his shoulder.
2. Hold the hoof pick in your right hand.
3. Bend your knees in a shallow squat next to your horse.

Make sure you're not kneeling too deeply to jump away if he yanks his hoof free and stomps down. Never sit or kneel on a stool or on the ground. (Therapy horses and many others can have their feet cleaned from a wheelchair. However, this requires special training and cooperation for both the horse and the seated person.)

4. Ask for your horse's hoof by doing any or all of the following:

- Run your fingers down the tendons on the back of his lower leg.
- Squeeze the tendons.
- Tap gently, then increasingly not so gently, with the prong of the hoof pick where the hoof meets the leg (the pastern). You are creating a mildly noxious stimulus from which the horse will eventually withdraw his foot, lifting it enough for you to take hold and support it.
- Gently squeeze his chestnut—the hard, rough growth above the "knee" on the inside of the legs.[1]
- Lean against his shoulder. If he doesn't lean back on you, he might become imbalanced enough for a split second that he will lift his foot.
- Cluck to him while doing any of the above. Some horses are trained to lift their feet to clucking or a voice command such as "Up!"
- Be ready to use your hand to catch and support the hoof as soon as it comes off the ground. Cup your hand under the hoof and proceed to clean it out. Use

1   What looks like the knee is actually the wrist in the forelegs and the ankle in the hind legs. The lower legs correspond to our fingers and toes. The hoof is a remnant of the horse's middle toe of the original five.

the pick to remove dirt, mud, manure, and pebbles along the edge of the hoof and in the V-shaped grooves of the frog.

Hind Leg Real-ease

When a horse first picks up a hind leg, there is a reflex spasticity in the tendons that causes her to retract her leg up toward her spine and in toward her belly. After a short while, the tendons release and the leg relaxes. Many handlers get into a pulling match with the horse rather than wait for the relaxation phase. But that release is a magical moment of mutual giving and receiving. You need to go along with the initial contraction and wait patiently for the drop while supporting the leg. Some horses release immediately, while other horses take five seconds or more. Sometimes there are two or more cycles of pulling back and releasing. After several grooming sessions with a handler who consistently waits for the release, most horses learn to let go immediately or become so relaxed that the reflex no longer gets triggered.

Feeling a horse's hind leg ease into your hands is like hearing a big sigh. It is a dance that becomes a metaphor for trust and patience in many life scenarios. Can you think of a situation where patience, trust, and synchronization with another's needs can create more happiness for you and them? After doing the hind leg release, look for an opportunity to do the same with a human in your life, especially yourself.

Massage—the 7th M of Grooming

The best tool we can use on horses is our hands, applied for petting and massaging. Equine massage is a profession, and some practitioners work on both humans and horses.

The Masterson Method and Tellington Touch are two of the most popular and effective techniques for massaging horses. Both Jim Masterson and Linda Tellington-Jones have cadres of certified practitioners who offer beginner workshops all over the world. Now is a good time to experience or re-experience a full-body massage for yourself with a professional body worker.[2]

Even without professional training, massaging a horse is an opportunity to tune in to your horse and go with your intuition. Try different strokes and experiment with what feels mutually satisfying.

1. Approach your horse with *con su permiso.*
2. Begin at the neck or shoulder.
3. Pretend you are petting any other animal, but avoid slapping or patting.
4. Use firm, confident strokes. With too light a touch, the horse may twitch her skin, as if you're a fly landing on her.
5. Try rubbing in small, slow circles with your thumb. (This is a Tellington Touch technique.)
6. Be mindful of signs that your horse would rather you not go there or has had enough. Although we humans might think a 60- to 90-minute full-body massage is the ultimate bliss, horses are usually done after a few minutes. Stay tuned to her facial expressions, especially ears and eyes. If she begins to lay back her

---

2   Well, not exactly *now*, at this writing. Now, winter 2020, we are at the peak of the covid-19 pandemic. Hopefully, by the time you read this, all the spas, gyms, pools, parks, beaches, schools, offices, and shops will be back to normal.

ears, widens her eyes, or wrings her tail, stop what you're doing and reassess.

7. Be mindful of signs that the horse is enjoying herself and releasing stress: whuffling, sighing, ears flopping out to the side, head dropping, eyelids lowering, licking and chewing motions, and yawning.

16

PHASE 3: *AM I BEING HERD?*

Leading, Following, and Partnering

Leading is not about being out in front.
It's about being in tune.

—Allan Hamilton, MD
Zen Mind, Zen Horse

L eading a horse is a metaphor for leading one's life. It calls
on our ability to show awareness, focus, determination,
clarity, and confidence—and to do so with the Inner
Smile that is part of our qigong practice. As with everything
about horsemanship and lifemanship, there are many ways
to lead, some more effective than others. No single way is
correct for all people and all horses. In the corporate world
I worked in, we spoke of *styles* of leadership ranging from
passive to consensus to dictatorial. I find it more difficult
to establish a place along that line in relation to animals
than in any other professional or social situation. In truth,
whether we are constitutionally bold or wimpy, there is no
one place to be on the spectrum. There is a range, a repertoire,
of situation-dependent behaviors. My personal quest for the

Right Stuff at the Right Place on the leadership continuum, with its paradoxes of situational dependency, is at the heart of my horsemanship.

Paradox

It's 3 p.m. on New Year's Eve Day, 1980, in the emergency room at San Francisco General Hospital (now Zuckerberg-of-Facebook San Francisco General Hospital and Trauma Center). Unbeknown to me, this night will go down in my personal history as the high point of my medical career. Today I am exactly six months, halfway, into my last year of residency. This is the fourth of what will be five elective E.R. rotations this year. I am only the second primary care house officer who has been allowed to function as a surgical resident emceeing the trauma rooms. (Of course, there is always an attending physician here too.) By mid-afternoon, all three trauma rooms are home to early revelers—a cardiac arrest from cocaine, a gunshot wound to an artery in the groin, and a young Moroccan woman who attempted suicide by ingesting stool specimen fluid that our poison control center tells us contains mercuric chloride, and that three days later—I visit her in the ICU—will result in massive, though reversible, kidney failure.

Within the next two hours, the trauma rooms are piled three deep with the severely ill and injured. All night, ambulances screech into the receiving bays, red lights flashing, wailing sirens winding down like placated cats. The chief of surgery, Frank Lewis, is humbly sewing up drunks in the boo-boo rooms while two fourth-year surgical residents and I get to tackle the major cases. I am in my element. I love the adrenalin, the teamwork, the chance to save lives, the stirrings of my five-star-general sub-personality.

I am a leader. The captain of my unit. I am authoritative, self-assured, clear, and consistent. I am confident, but not cocky, in my knowledge and experience. I give clear, crisp, yet respectful orders as I deploy my cadre of nurses, respiratory techs, and interns in mission-critical situations. Each person has a role. There is no designated hierarchy, but for most protocols, the MD gives the orders. A decade later, this would be the material of medical TV. And while I don't hesitate to call in the attending when needed, I know my stuff: stuff backed up by science. There are many unknowns and variables, but the evidence-based interventions are mostly knowable, predictable, and life saving. I hear then, and to this day, the words of our attending, later UCSF Chief of Surgery Bill Shechter: "A surgeon is sometimes right, never in doubt." You react quickly and act decisively. You take risks.

Forty years later, I'm riding Serena in the round ring. Her canter departs are tense and emotional like Tallulah Bankhead, the drama queen she might have been named for. A Barpasser granddaughter from a long line of champion show horses, Serena evidently rejected that destiny. I don't know much about her history, but the story goes that she was passed down among several owners after failing—refusing—to develop the requisite shlumpy Western Pleasure gaits. I am unable to get her to lope quietly and I am angst-thick with the ethical question of whether I should even ask her to do and be this thing that she is not. Doctor Decisive is OTC (off the case). Little Miss Uncertainty is on call. She has philosophical issues with asking such a large, gentle animal to bend to her will, to go when, where, and how she commands. I think I am risking the loss of her trust, the slowly nurtured assurance that I will not cowboy around on her like some yahoo on the show circuit. There are no scientific studies that prove the best outcomes on the horse-human permissiveness-dominance scale.

I turn to gifted interspecies communicator Nancy Windheart and ask her to talk with Serena about my conundrum. Early in the session, Nancy relates that Serena has had extensive, sometimes harsh, training with many different owners and trainers.

> Some of the training she had was respectful and decent, some of it was not. Some of it was dominance-style training and she very much internally rebelled against being forced to do everything. However, she's used to people telling her what to do. That's the world she's been in. She understands that. There's the parts of her that rebel against that. But she also doesn't want to be responsible for making all the decisions, either. That's scary for her.
>
> Another way to say it, Beverley, is that she can understand and hold that you are equal partners in your relationship and that there are times when she's going to need to listen to you and you're going to need to tell her what to do. She can hold that. And what she wants from you is clarity about which role you're in.

To be clear with Serena, I must be clear with myself, and that is a work in progress. We are coming into our own, seeking that place of softness, willingness, and balance of wills. Natural horsemanship clinician John Lyons has said that the horse-human relationship is a 51 percent–49 percent proposition: sometimes the human leads 51 percent, sometimes the horse does. Many a rider is alive today because she deferred to the trail horse who refused to go where there was a cougar or a quagmire. The Pioneer Saloon here in Woodside has a rough-hewn log hitching rail. Some patrons ride into town on Friday nights like it was the 1880s. After one too many, they mount up and let their horses be the designated drivers.

Horses Leading Horses

We are doing Phase 3, herd observation, in a private Equine-imity session. My Inner Smile is beaming; I feel profoundly blessed to be able to share my love of horses. We are standing outside the 100-foot-square catch corral, watching two horses walk in tandem. One is in front, and one is behind with her nose near the front horse's rump. So here, in good humor, is the one trick question I ever ask: "Which horse is the leader?" Inevitably someone new to horses will guess it's the horse in front. However, it's just the opposite.

Dominant horses lead (push) submissive horses from behind by laying back their ears and putting line-of-sight pressure on the front horse's rump. In Traditional Chinese Medicine, the eyes are said to emit powerful rays of ch'i. Seeing how dogs and cats react to being stared at, and seeing how horses move eachother eye-on-rump, we become believers in eye ch'i. If Horse A sees a more dominant Horse B come up behind him with ears pinned back, Horse A will move away from Horse B. Often these signals are too subtle for humans to notice. For horses who know eachother well, a tiny flick of an ear sends the message.

Dominance in herd dynamics carries none of the ego-feeding connotations that humans invest in that word. A dominant horse is responsible for the well-being of the herd. She isn't given the corner office or 100,000 stock options. In the wild, the pecking order is more or less stable. Food, water, and space are abundant. Social groupings and mating pairs are well established, and in fact inherited from the mother. In a domestic herd, with members coming and going on a monthly, daily, or hourly basis, there is more plasticity—and more stress—in the rankings. There is competition for food, water, and real estate, and there are shifting permutations of buddies. And while horses don't unFriend their exes on Facebook, there is emotional disruption, and a readjustment period, when a new horse moves in, or when someone is taken out for lessons, rides, vet or farrier, or moves off the ranch.

People Leading Horses—Dominance, Respect, Kindness

In every interaction with horses, we are, at different times, the leader, partner, or follower. The role we choose depends on our personality and on the situation at hand. Equestrian attitudes range from ultra-permissiveness to stern discipline to dominance to violence. While most of us in most horse-human scenarios fall mid-spectrum, at least a couple of prominent natural horsemanship (NH) trainers have been outed on YouTube for arguably bullying behaviors.

Many in the horse world, even kindly NH practitioners, insist that the human must always act as the alpha horse. Alpha is defined as displaying dominance and demanding respect, especially respect for boundaries and "space." However, as we saw from Jan's experience in chapter 12, it's tricky to place one's alpha bet at the right place on the table.

Chapter 6, Whoa Nellie, teaches that horses feel more secure and less stressed when they have a consistent place in the pecking order. They rely on a strong leader, usually a mare, to make decisions and keep the herd safe. However, horses do not for a minute think that humans are just smaller, smarter horses. They learn from their Day 1 on earth that we do not engage with them like their mamas and mates, that we are not even a reasonable facsimile of another horse. Our cultural appropriation of the Equus language is pidgin at best. Our attempts at leadership are by our rules, not theirs, no matter how much we observe and mimic them. In fact, a fascinating study by Smith and others shows that horses prefer humans who take a submissive posture.[1]

Underlying our decisions about being alpha are issues of personal boundaries and self-esteem. In every relationship in life, including with one's self, each person has to settle boundary disputes. How far into your personal space do you allow a stranger to come? A friend? To what extent does your stress come from letting others impose on you for favors and sacrifices? Is standing up for yourself more stressful than avoiding confrontation at all costs? However we answer these questions, we tend to carry these internal dramas over to our relationships with people, pets, and horses.[2] Because horses are large yet easily intimidated, we can use overtraining and overpowering them as compensation for areas of our lives where we lack control, self-confidence, or self-respect.

A key element in seeking to have one's leadership and autonomy recognized is the fear that like Rodney Dangerfield, we don't get no respect. You might hear an instructor insist, "Make that horse respect you!" However, as Mark Rashid points out, horses don't have sufficient development in the neocortex of the brain to understand the abstract concept of

---

1   Smith AV et al. Domestic horses (Equus caballus) prefer to approach humans displaying a submissive body posture rather than a dominant body posture. *Anim Cogn.* 2018; 21:307-312.

2   In psychology, carrying over dynamics from one relationship to another is called *transference.*

respect. Good and bad, right and wrong are also abstractions that horses do not conceptualize. When we correct them for what we consider bad or wrong behavior, they do not recalibrate some linguistically informed moral compass. They are simply learning the patterning we impose on them from our value system. We lead them into our ways and they follow. If our leadership is firm, kind, consistent, and unambiguous, the horse develops trust.

While a professional trainer can establish leadership, or at least dominance, in a matter of minutes, it may take as long as two years to develop deep trust between horse and human. The predominance of kindness in our interactions is the basis for trust. In the world of Cowboy Dressage pioneer Eitan Beth-Halachmy, an ounce of kindness is worth a pound of dominance.

Principles and Particulars

The principles of leading horses, and one's life, can be summarized in the mnemonic of the three Hs and the three Cs. Effective leadership engages your:

- _H_ead, the mental _concept_ of your goal, where you want to go
- _H_eart, the emotional _commitment_ to your journey
- _H_ara (dan tien), the _core strength_ that mobilizes your personal power

The particulars of safe leadership are:

- Make sure the lead rope is off the ground where neither you nor the horse (nor your mentor) can trip on it.

- Do not wind the lead rope around your hand. In that configuration, if the horse needs to take off suddenly, he can take you with him. You surely want to leave the ranch with the same number of fingers you drove in with. Hold the rope in a figure 8, folded in your palm but not coiled in a circle.
- Many trainers, and I, recommend leading your horse by placing yourself parallel to her neck, between her ear and her shoulder. This position allows you to see her head and ears and note where her attention is. That way, if you notice that something begins to worry her, like a flapping tarp, you can act as her security and offer reassurance. If her worry is enough to cause a spook, you will be able to move accordingly and avoid getting stepped on or pushed aside.

From a bioenergetic perspective, walking between your horse's ear and shoulder is the best way to blend your ch'i. In this way, you lead your horse with both energy and body language, like the boy in the illustration.

The particulars of effective leadership are:

- *Do not drag or pull the horse.* Pulling your horse by his head is an act of impatience, not of kindness, though we are all guilty of it at times. If the horse resists your request for forward motion, drive her from behind like a dominant horse would do. Going up the volume "V" as described in chapter 12, progress from using ch'i, to body language, to a flick of the lead rope or wand on your horse's rump. Horses quickly learn to follow body language and ch'i with, for example, an index finger aimed in the direction of travel.

- *Do not let the horse drag or pull you.* A horse who is intent on going forward faster than you want to go, or to a different destination, should be corrected for the pace and place you wish. Rather than yanking continually on the lead rope, you should redirect the horse's overly forward energy by moving him in a circle around you, bringing him back to your side. You might have to do this repeatedly, plus stop and back up, until he learns to stay alongside you. Two principles are in effect here: One is to not try to bottle up a horse's energy, but instead to re-channel it. The other is to make the desired behavior easy and the undesired behavior annoying. Your horse will learn that it's too bothersome to keep going in a circle each time he pulls on you. Because these maneuvers require a high degree of feel and finesse, your mentor should help you redirect, correct, and reconnect with your horse.

- *Look where you're going,* not at the horse, not at the ground. Keep your eye on the destination, the goal. Head, heart, and hara should be aligned for this purpose. Do not look back while tugging forward. If you look back at the horse's face, stop your feet. If you look back while trying to walk forward, you will be giving her mixed messages. Staring at a prey animal is often a signal for her to stop and retreat, and many horses are trained to back up this way.

Ideally you should be able to lead the horse from either her left or right side. As you change sides, notice the difference in energy, softness, and feel from one side to the other. Initially, you will want to lead your horse with a halter and lead rope. After you have bonded, she can learn to stay with you without a material connection.

Dan Tien Leading

The 1906 Picasso painting at the beginning of this chapter is titled *Boy Leading a Horse.* We could also call it *Boy Leading a Horse with Ch'i.* The naked horse and the naked boy are in mystical communication with an invisible energy between them. The boy's right hand is positioned at the horse's chest as if holding a lead rope. His left hand is at his navel. We can imagine that the two bodies are connected by a beam of ch'i radiating from their dan tien centers. Horse and boy both have the right foot stepping forward and the left foot back, walking in harmony with calm, deliberate motion. The horse seems as tuned in to the boy as he would be to another horse. The landscape is barren, desert like, unpopulated, reminiscent of Antoine de Saint-Exupéry's Little Prince and the fox, who tamed eachother in the Sahara.

Each year around the first week of December, the lesson herd is let out of their summer pasture to their adjoining winter pasture. When the gate is opened, seventy horses gallop into the field and continue an exuberant run back and forth in 200-yard laps. Remarkably, much of the herd runs in formation, turning abruptly with eachother like a school of fish. We humans watching from the sidelines with our video phones can only wonder at the instantaneous signaling that allows this simultaneous motion.

Whatever the cues are among the herd, we can assume that horses are similarly tuned in to us. So whether you are leading your horse with or without a rope, become sensitive to the body language between you. When you lead:

- Shine your dan tien like a flashlight on your destination.
- Be clear with your intention to get somewhere, even if it's in a circle.
- Make your body follow your intention.
- If you and your horse are not in a feel-good dance of motion, *stop*. Be in a dance of synchronized stillness until you are ready to walk together in harmony. If your horse is too agitated or frisky to stop, engage your mentor for handling.

You will use the physical act of leading in most of your activities with horses. You will use the principles of leading horses, from head, heart, and hara, in most of your activities in life.

17

PHASE 4: THE MEDITATION RIDE

Qigong on Horseback

To be engrossed by something outside ourselves is a powerful antidote for the rational mind.

— Anne Lamott, *Bird by Bird*

All the activities described thus far allow us to be deeply engrossed by things outside ourselves. Time spent with horses feels like time out of time. If we do nothing more than the three non-riding engrossments, *dayenu*. Dayenu ("dah-YAY-noo") is a 1,000-year-old Passover song. It means "enough for us." Its fifteen verses recount the litany of miracles, any one of which would have been dayenu, that the God of the Israelites enacted to take them out of Egypt and, forty years later, into the Promised Land.

While it won't take you forty years to get from the wu

ji pose to the back of a horse, if all you care to do is meet, groom, and go for walks with your horse, *dayenu*. Those activities are enough to experience most of the benefits of companionship with horses.

However, for me, the most engrossing antidote for the overrational mind and the heavy heart is riding. When I'm on top of a horse, negative thoughts and emotions ride off into the sunset. I am full of, focused on, pleasant body sensations. The rich sensory input from the oneness of our centaurship overtakes worry and sadness. Physical complaints can also disappear.

There is even less mental activity needed, and more sensory input available, when someone else is leading your horse. After the injury described in the introduction, when I became a client at a therapeutic riding (TR) center, I had no reins or saddle. The horse handler, directed by the therapeutic riding instructor (TRI), led us around. I felt relaxed and pampered. It was like the difference between washing my own hair and lying back at the sink in a salon.

For this reason, the meditation ride in the fourth phase of Equine-imity uses a therapeutic riding configuration with bareback pads. In the twelve-person class, four humans and one horse team up for riding rotations in the round ring. The person on the horse can just "Leave the Driving to Us" while she revels, often for the first time, in the rhythms of the big, moving animal underneath her. We perform the Wu Duan Jin at a halt, then continue into a walking meditation, maintaining the wu ji posture and dan tien breathing. To add to the sensory mix, we create gentle centrifugal forces by making slow, sweeping turns in a yin-and-yang pattern. In the background—actually in the middle of the arena on a barrel—we play Nawang Khechog's *Music as Medicine* Tibetan flute on a wireless speaker. While no horse has ever objected to the equipment or to the soothing sounds, it's a good idea to acclimate them to the setup before you get on.

Also before getting on, you will reprise the first three phases of Equine-imity—meet and greet, grooming, and leading. Let your horse get a sense of you on the ground.

Any riding instructor or other mentor can choreograph the meditation ride if she is willing, has a suitable horse, and is in tune with the philosophy and health benefits of this type of riding. You might also be able to experience this activity at a therapeutic riding center. I have conducted Equine-imity for TRIs and other riding instructors for the purpose of their being able to use it with their students. If you do the meditation ride outside of a traditionally configured TR session, I recommend that you have at least one person to focus on, and lead, the horse and one person, your mentor, to focus on you.

If you have the option to bring your own music, choose something relaxing or uplifting. Not to say that it couldn't make for a fine uplift, but heavy metal shred guitar would not be my first choice for meditation. State-based learning being what it is, when you go home and play the music again, your body will be transported back to your peaceful ride.

When dismounting, take respectful and affectionate leave. Lead her home, brush her off, recheck her feet, part with heart. Bask in the meditative mood you created together.

Many Equine-imity students go on to take conventional riding lessons. The most accessible way for you to go a-horseback might be a commercial trail ride. You can ride any horse in a dude string in wu ji posture, using your dan tien breathing, soft eyes, and Inner Smile.

18

Happy Trails to You

*I*n this book I've shared with you my personal journey with horses and my gratitude for how horses enrich us somatically, emotionally, spiritually, and mentally. The core message of *Equine-imity* is that our experience of stress comes primarily from negative thoughts and emotions. While feelings of stress are understandable and appropriate given the hardships of external events in a world beyond our control, we *can* learn ways to temper our internal reactions. Restoration of equanimity is best achieved with the other functions in the Jungian quaternity that are complementary to intellect and emotion: our somato-sensory and intuitive, including psychic-spiritual, abilities. Once we have disabused ourselves of any prejudices against our bodies, the somatic function becomes most liberating in counteracting stress. Moving meditations such as qigong, tai ji, yoga, and dance create positive somato-spiritual experiences with proven health benefits.

Horses are the ideal beings to teach us both quietude in motion and exuberance in stillness. From them, we learn to be comfortable in our bodies, to reconnect with nature, to trust our instincts, and to return to our state of original grace.

Even if you do not pursue horsemanship or meditation

213

long term, you will have learned some attitudinal, philosophic, and somatic techniques to use in whatever situations or activities you encounter.

If you do wish to continue to explore horsemanship as a meditation or as a career, appendix D, EAATing at the Grownup Table, will start you on that path.

As a follow-on to this book, I am preparing a manual for horse owners and equine-assisted activities and therapies providers. With this manual, equestrians and equine professionals will be able to replicate the Stanford Equine-imity Program at their own barns and learning centers. The manual will be available for download on my website at http://www. horsensei.com.

May the trail rise up to greet you as you ride
May the stars reach down and touch you with their light
May the tumbleweeds at play
Keep you company by day
And coyotes serenade you through the night

May no river be too rapid or too wide
May no mountain be too high for you to climb
May your pony serve you well
And take you home to your corral
May the spirit of the prairie be your guide

Friends don't let friends ride away without good wishes
Friends don't let friends ride away without a song
A good wish or two may come in handy
somewhere down the trail
So take mine with you now as you ride along

May you live a happy life on cowboy time
May the winds of change be gentle as you ride
Someday soon I don't know when
We'll meet again but until then
May the trail rise up to greet you as you ride.

Dave Stamey and Liz Anderson,
"May the Trail Rise Up to Greet You,"
Tonopah

(Used with permission)

Appendix A: Body English, Body Chinese — Ch'i, Qi, Ji, and Dao

Qi, Chi, Ch'i, and Ji

Non–Chinese speakers confuse "ji," "chi," and "ch'i." and get even more confused when they see "qi." In the fractured phonetics of the relatively recent pinyin Romanization, vital energy is spelled "qi" and pronounced "chee." Before pinyin was adopted, English used the Wade-Giles spelling, "ch'i," also pronounced "chee." The apostrophe means the "ch" is aspirated and pronounced like the "ch" in "cheese."

"Ji" ("jee") in pinyin means *pole* and refers to the pole-less-ness of the *wu ji* (the Great Nothingness, the No Polarity), and to the opposite pole-arities of yin and yang in the *tai ji* (the Great Polarity). In Wade-Giles, pole was spelled "chi" and, unaspirated without the apostrophe, also pronounced "jee."

We see similar differences in the "t" words from Chinese used in this book. In Wade-Giles, "t" is pronounced like the English "d," so "Taoism" is pronounced "Dow-ism," which pinyin spells "Daoism." In Wade-Giles, the aspirated "t" has an apostrophe, so the martial art form becomes "t'ai chi," pronounced "tie jee."

Wu ji, tai ji, and yin and yang are important concepts in

Daoist cosmology. They describe the human body in relation to the origins and infinite space-time properties of the universe and to the ch'i that permeates, some say composes, all things.

In this book, I have used the spellings that are easiest to pronounce for native English speakers, whether from Wade-Giles or pinyin. An exception is the pinyin "qigong," which is spelled thus in almost all references to it, and for which the reader is asked to learn to pronounce "chee goong."

Ji. Pole, roof, highest point, extreme, earth's (magnetic) pole, (anode or cathode electrical) pole. The Chinese character for ji—木—contains the radical for wood.

Wu ji. The Great Nothingness. No polarity. In Western cosmological terms, the universe before the Big Bang. In theological terms, the mind of God before Creation.

Tai ji. The ultimate polarity, where the wu ji polarizes into yin and yang.

Qi (ch'i, "chee"). Breath, air, vital energy. Composed of the root words for rice 米 and steam 气. In ancient times, qi referred to steam rising from a bowl of rice.

In *tai ji* and *qigong*, we cultivate *ch'i* starting in the *wu ji* posture and entering the *tai ji* to commence dan tien belly breathing.

The Dao ("Dow")

 As we saw in chapter 8, the Dao is synonymous with the wu ji. It is also translated as the Way, meaning the correct, harmonious, moral and spiritual path. The Chinese character to the left illustrates that journey. The right-hand ideogram is the character for head, 首, in the sense of a chief or director. The left-hand ideogram depicts a boatman ferrying the Mind on the Way. *The Tao of Equus* book and the Way of the Horse divination cards use these concepts to teach the philosophy of being on a spiritual path with horses.

Appendix B: The History and Nature of Energy—Physics and Metaphysics

A Panel Discussion of the San Francisco Parapsychology Research Group, May 1988 with Saul-Paul Sirag[1]

Chapter 8, The Ch'i Also Rises, presents the bioenergetics of ch'i and reiki. I noted that the National Center for Complementary and Integrative Health acknowledges the validity of qigong as energy medicine and recognizes two types of energy: veritable, which can be measured, and putative, which has not yet been measured.

Although the terms ch'i and reiki are not mentioned by this PRG panel, it was convened in response to debates on the differences—historical, experimental, and semantic—between veritable energy, such as electricity, and putative forms, such as ch'i. The discussion pertains to the meaning of energy and energy fields in physics, philosophy, martial arts, and healing. At the time, 1988,

---

1   Excerpted from Targ R, Radin D, Millay J (eds.) *Radiant Minds: Scientists Explore the Dimensions of Consciousness*. Jean Millay. October 10, 2010. Originally published as *Silver Threads:25 Years of Parapsychology Research*. Kane B, Brown D, Millay J (eds.) (Westport, CT: Praeger, 1993).

even parapsychologists experimenting with ESP and UFO sightings considered some uses of the word energy to be "New Age" and "flaky"—terms that appear in the discussion.

Some latter-day heirs to New Age thinking have been intimidated by scientism and its theology of evidence-based medicine. So in an effort to make a scientific case for the value of loving over thinking, they cite misinterpreted biophysical measurements to claim that veritable heart energy fields are stronger than veritable brain energy fields. This point of view is popular among those wishing to validate heart-centered psychotherapies, especially equine-assisted forms. However, as we've noted, the EKG does not measure love and the EEG does not translate thoughts. The putative energies of all Four Ways of Wisdom—heart, mind, body, imagination—are equally strong and important.

Exploration of these ideas remains vital as we seek to better understand the nature of ch'i, reiki, and energy centers like the dan tien. In the meantime, we can validate the effects of ch'i and reiki for ourselves, whether or not science can, or ever will, explain our experiences.

Saul-Paul Sirag: I want to talk about something perhaps more mundane,[2] which is *energy*. The reason for this is that Russell [Targ, world-renowned remote viewing researcher and laser physicist] has been complaining about people's use of the word "energy." At least he complained once to Jean [Millay, psychologist and parapsychologist, 1929–2017] about somebody using the term *psychic energy*, and so I thought that it might be a good idea to give a brief presentation on what physicists mean by energy and how energy came into the physicist's lexicon and how that might relate to explanations

---

2 More mundane than the lofty metaphysical discussion of the nature of reality in the previous hour's panel discussion.

of psi[3] or non-explanations of psi, as the case may be.

So I studied up a little bit on the history of energy in physics, and actually I was quite surprised. I brought with me an old physics book [*holds up book*]. I collect old physics books; whenever I see one, I buy one. This one is quite old, published in 1837, and one of the most interesting things about it is that the word energy doesn't occur anywhere in it. [*Audience laughter.*] Now, that corresponds to the fact that there wasn't a physics of energy in 1837. You might think that this is just a book that was at a high school level, and so it wasn't really up with the current physics of even 1837. But actually how energy came into physics is an amazing story.

Newtonian mechanics is, in a sense, the beginning of real physics. Of course, the Greeks talked about physics—they invented the word, they invented the concept, and so on—but there wasn't really a mathematical body of theory. There were some mathematical formulas that the Greeks knew, but they didn't amount to much. We really think of physics as starting with Newton's equations.

One of the interesting things about Newton's work for us here—and it's frequently overlooked because ever since Fritjof Capra's book [*The Tao of Physics*] came out, Newton has been made sort of the bad guy [*audience laughter*] who made the world mechanistic and deterministic, and in the twentieth century, quantum mechanics comes along and rescues us from all that [*audience laughter*]—that's the short version of the Capra book. [*Loud audience laughter.*] Capra wasn't the only one saying that; lots of people have said that, but he said it very eloquently, and so a lot of people have that view of the history of physics.

But as a matter of fact, Newton's equations were, in a

---

3   Psi is short for psychic phenomena or paranormal ability.

sense, a very magical set of equations because there was really no model, there was no *mechanism* whatsoever in Newton's equations. Newton's equations imply instantaneous action at a distance. He was severely criticized for this in his day, and it was in that context that he very angrily said, "I don't make hypotheses." Of course he made hypotheses, but he meant that he didn't have an underlying model. "There are no strings attached between the moon and the earth; how in the world can the moon affect the tides?" That's what people said. In fact, the French described Newton's theory as an *occult* theory for that reason because he had an occult force that acted at a distance instantaneously.

Actually, Newton realized that that was a lack in his theory, that there wasn't any underlying mechanism whatsoever. What he really believed, and what he said, was that space is God's sensorium. So in other words, his explanation for why the equations worked was that God made them work, so it was totally magic. However, people became familiar with those equations, and what happens when you become familiar is that the very familiarity makes it seem ordinary, makes it seem unmagical.

So it became sort of the paradigm of a mechanistic theory, and as I say, it's not mechanistic at all. However, the aspect of it that is important, which is what really impressed people, is that it was completely *deterministic*. That is to say, if you knew the positions of the planets at one point in time, then you knew the positions of the planets at any point in time. You just had to crank through the equations and you would get the position. Of course, you couldn't do it very far into the future in those days because they didn't have computers yet, but with computers and with improved mathematical techniques, we can do that quite handily.

But those are just details. The important thing is the matter of principle. The theory was, in principle, deterministic. So at first, there was a kind of worship, an awe of Newton, once people got over the shock of how magical the equations were. There was a kind of awe at the determinism, the perfect determinism of the equations, and of course, they were very successful. There were even books published that were the analog of Capra's book in the sense that they said that Newton's equations were a way of seeing the mind of God. In other words, physics at that time was being used as a way of supporting certain religious ideas. Newton himself thought of his equations that way, and other people did very much.

After about a hundred years of that, a reaction started setting in due largely to poets and philosophers like Blake who were objecting to the stifling feeling that came from the philosophy of determinism, the idea that everything was set from the word go, so to speak. Blake wrote many lines of poetry about Newton—I think he has a long poem called *Newton*, in which he asks to be saved from Newton's "sleep." I think it was, "God save us from single vision and Newton's sleep." What Blake meant by that was an opposition to the supposed determinism of the universe. Determinism portrays the universe as merely clockwork—that was the catchword for Newton's theory. Newton himself didn't say that, of course, because Newton was all too aware that there wasn't any clock-like mechanism. A clock is a beautiful mechanism, whereas the planets are not. The only analogy that is valid there is the fact that a clock is deterministic and Newton's laws regarding the planets are deterministic, but otherwise, the analogy totally breaks down. The clockwork is kind of like a dead thing because once it's wound up, it just goes on until it winds down, and that's the end of the world, presumably.

A reaction set in, among the Romantic poets especially, and an interesting thing is that out of this Romantic reaction to Newton's determinism, the word "energy" started being bandied about, particularly among these philosophers and Romantic poets.

Psychologist A: Did Newton use the word "energy"?

Saul-Paul Sirag: No, Newton never used the word "energy."

Physicist A[4]: When was [the term] "kinetic energy" invented?[5]

Saul-Paul Sirag: *[smiling]* I'm gonna tell about that! *[Audience laughter.]* No, there's no kinetic energy in Newton's work. It's all a matter of force, F=MA, and the force of gravity obeying the inverse square law.[6] That's essentially Newton's theory of gravity, and it's not a field theory. It's an action-at-a-distance theory.

Actually, "energy" wasn't at first used in the physics context, that's the point I'm making. It was used in a personal

---

4   [Russell Targ. Footnotes in brackets are not in *Silver Threads*. They are added in this book.]

5   In 1807, Thomas Young proposed the name "energy" for mass times velocity squared. However, "energy" was considered too disreputable a term by most physicists until the 1840s.

6   [The inverse square law, Energy = $1/distance^2$, states that an energy field becomes weaker the further you get from its source. If you move 2 inches from the heart, the signal is 2^2, or 4 times, weaker than the EKG signal with an electrode on the skin. This principle is especially important in theories of reiki and in studies of intercessory prayer, as the prayer "signal" does not seem to get weaker over long distances.]

context, that is to say, a personal freedom context, the romantic context, literally.

Physicist B: What did the word mean?

Saul-Paul Sirag: *Ergon* means *work*, and energy is the ability to do work. It's the feeling of being able to move freely. It's the opposite of the feeling of determinism, I suppose. And it's a feeling of vitality.

Physicist C [7]: Like he says, *"Energy is pure delight."*

Saul-Paul Sirag: Yes, that is from Blake. The term really arose in that context, and the only scientists who were thinking along the lines of an energy paradigm, you might say, were really fringe scientists in that period.

There was a German doctor named Mayer who is supposedly the discoverer of the conservation of energy. But the way he discovered it was, as you might guess, by paying attention to food, feeding rats, and weighing things. Of course, it was a rough kind of measurement that he could do in that way at that time, and he did crude little experiments that improved a little bit over the years. But he had a hard time getting that work published. When his paper was published in 1842—that explains why there's no "energy" in here [*taps the 1837 physics book*] whatsoever—hardly anybody knew that the thing was published. It wasn't published in the major journals at that time; several major journals turned down his paper.

Then in England, Prescott Joule, a self-taught amateur

---

7   [The late Dean Brown, PhD, physicist, SRI International parapsychology researcher, poet, scholar.]

experimenter, was also independently trying to understand energy. One of the things that was the impetus for his work was the development at the time of machinery that used energy in our terms today, like the steam engine, which was an important machine. But you see, the steam engine was invented by James Watt, who knew no physics whatsoever. I mean, these were just inventors, they were really fringe people; they didn't know Newton's equations. Newton's equations wouldn't have helped them one iota anyway. Knowing Newton's equations, you couldn't build a steam engine. There's nothing in there that helps you. Nothing about heat.

In other words, the concept of energy arises in the context of thinking about heat. And the problem with heat is that it's subjective, before you have any equipment, before a thermometer is invented, let's say. Heat is a feeling, after all—you feel hot, you feel warm. You can have two people in the same room—one guy says it's hot, and the other guy says it's cold. [*Audience laughter*.] You know that problem—one guy wants the window open, the other guy wants it closed. So how can you make a science out of something so subjective as temperature—the feeling of heat?

So energy was gradually brought into the realm of physics by people like Mayer and, especially, Joule. By the way, our unit of energy in the metric system is the joule, which is one watt-second, if that means anything to you. It's not a large amount of energy, if you think about how many kilowatts of electricity you use in a day.

What Joule was able to do was to make energy respectable by doing a simple, ingenious experiment that showed an exact correspondence between the amount of heat energy and the amount of mechanical energy. In other words, he was able to define a notion of mechanical energy. He did several kinds of experiments, but I suppose his most important experiment along that line was just having a paddle moving very slowly in water or oil and measuring the change in temperature of the water as the paddle rotated a certain number of times. These were long, laborious experiments that he did, and you can imagine that the statistics on them were poor. He had to do many, many runs. It was very much like an ESP experiment [*audience laughter*] in the sense that he did many runs and he got wildly different numbers and he just averaged them to come out with these equivalences.

Hardly anybody was interested in that work. It just seemed too far off the beaten path. Joule read his paper at a scientific meeting, and no one was interested in his first experiment. So he got permission to read another paper a couple of years later when he'd improved his experiments a lot. And since there hadn't been any interest in his first paper, they were only going to give him ten minutes to read this paper in the midst of a lot of other papers being given. Fortunately, in the audience of that second paper of his was an up-and-coming 23-year-old physicist, a guy who became Lord Kelvin later on, and he saw the significance of this paper. He gave Joule a lot of feedback from the audience and then went off and did his own experiments and really developed the whole field of heat. So we have the Kelvin temperature scale, and the unit of heat in absolute units is the Kelvin.

Now the point of all this is to show how physics is a kind of a living being in a sense—it feeds on ideas and it grows. There are lots of prejudices in it, of course, but new ideas come into it, many times from the fringes of physics. A new idea comes in and gets calibrated in some way that makes sense to the rest of physics when it makes contact with some existing part of physics—not necessarily with all of physics because physics, especially at that time, was compartmentalized.

For instance, there were at the same time in the early 1800s important developments going on in electricity and magnetism. It was in 1820 that Oersted first discovered that electricity and magnetism had something to do with each other. In fact, this book [in Saul-Paul's hand], published in 1837—so this is, of course, after 1820—ends with a short section on electricity and a short section on magnetism, and there's not the slightest hint that the two have anything to do with each other. So this book is quite behind the times [*audience laughter*] so far as electricity and magnetism are concerned but …

Psychologist B [8]: … Saul-Paul, I found a school textbook while I was looking for science textbooks that didn't seem to think that they had anything to do with each other, either. They had different sections on each one, and there was nothing that would pull the whole electromagnetic spectrum together even in this textbook recently published for junior high school students.

Saul-Paul Sirag: Well, this book came long before Maxwell's electromagnetic spectrum was invented in the late 1800s. Oersted's work was quite startling, and it took a long time for it to get into the textbooks, obviously, but the point I'm making here is that energy didn't immediately have to hook up with electromagnetism—it wouldn't have helped it much to hook up immediately with electricity and magnetism because that was a pretty far out field anyway. It had to hook up with something that was absolutely staid and established, which was mechanics, Newtonian mechanics.

8 [The late Jean Millay, PhD.]

It was then, in thinking about heat, that the idea of kinetic energy comes in. You see there was a theory developed about that time called the *kinetic theory of heat.* This was the idea that heat is due to the random motion of atoms or small particles of some kind, that is, due to the random kinetic energy of those particles. So really kinetic energy comes into the picture first by way of heat and then it gets generalized by way of the work of Joule. That is to say, the notion of energy gets generalized, so that it includes not just kinetic energy but potential energy. That's how energy comes into the discussion of gravity, by way of potential energy.

Physicist A: When did that happen?

Saul-Paul Sirag: In the early 1800s. Joule and Kelvin had a lot to do with that. For instance, I can give this book a charge— [New Age] people talk about *charging*—giving something an energy charge, maybe by staring at it—a flaky use of the word energy—but I can give this thing a charge simply by lifting it [lifts book off the table]. Now it has more potential energy than it had down here on the table because I lifted it in the gravitational field.

Now, Newton didn't have the notion of a gravitational field. Remember, Newton's idea was that gravity worked totally by action at a distance. There's no field involved, so the field idea comes in by way of the energy idea. It actually comes in by way of potential energy, and what we say is that the potential energy is actually stored in the gravitational field. So when I lift it up, this thing here has potential energy because of where it is in the gravitational field. Now, if I drop it [*drops book on the table with a clunk*], that potential energy is, we say in physics, transformed into kinetic energy.

So the field idea became useful in physics with the idea of potential energy being transformed into kinetic energy and doing work with that kinetic energy, and gradually, the field idea took over physics, especially in the hands of Maxwell. In the late nineteenth century, he used the field idea—the electric field idea and the magnetic field idea—to understand light itself.

[...]

So the point of this history is simply that an idea that seemed flaky at first became the key idea in all realms of physics. One can't predict exactly what the future of physics will be. It could even happen that some better idea will come along and eclipse the field idea, but right now, it looks like that idea is very solid and will be here to stay.

Let me just stop there. There are lots of different things that can be said, but I'll answer some questions.

[...]

Psychologist B: I'm really interested in all this, but one of the reasons I particularly wanted you to discuss energy is because of our original argument about energy: when spiritual healers say that they are going to "put energy through" somebody, the physicists say no, no, that's not what energy is. I really wanted to talk about the semantics problem between physics and the psi realm. People who do spiritual healing or people who are exploring these realms seem to be quite at ease with using the word "energy." What word should they use instead?

Saul-Paul Sirag: Well, maybe you're misunderstanding me. I'm not saying that they shouldn't use the word "energy" at all. I'm just saying ...

Psychologist B: ... a lot of people tell me I shouldn't use that word ...

Saul-Paul Sirag: ... what I'm saying is that you shouldn't use the word "energy" in that context and think that you necessarily mean the same thing the physicist means by it.

Psychologist A: How would we discriminate between those two concepts, the physics concept and the New Age concept?

Saul-Paul Sirag: Well, you have to make the point I just stated. But there's another point I want to make that I think is equally important. Remember, Newton didn't discover energy, smart as he was. All the people who were contemporary with him were smart too, and they didn't discover the notion of energy. One of the peculiar things about the notion of energy and one of the reasons that the idea of energy was discovered so late in physics is that it's invisible, it's a behind-the-scenes kind of thing, and ...

Physicist B: They just called it "work." Work is force times distance.[9] They had energy back then, it was just a different name.

Saul-Paul Sirag: Well, energy is related to work but it's different.

---

9   The idea of *force times distance* as an independent concept called *work* (and other names) was introduced in the 1820s after "energy" was proposed for mass times velocity squared (1807). See Thomas Kuhn, *The Essential Tension* (Chicago: University of Chicago Press, 1977), 84.

Psychologist B: When [Physicist C] was quoting Blake's equating energy with pure joy, we saw that Blake was using "energy" in the psychological sense before physicists came along and grabbed the word away from us.

Saul-Paul Sirag: Well, we used the word heat in a psychological sense before physicists gave precise notions of heat by inventing thermometers. But the point I want to make here is that the principle of the conservation of energy is interesting from the point of view that you're raising. Healers talk about putting "energy" into things. One thing that you have to realize is that we in physics use principles like conservation of energy to discover new forms of energy because we can use it as a bookkeeping criterion. If we do an experiment in a confined region, which means that we're able to keep track of all the energy flows, so to speak, and we find that our numbers just don't add up, that there's something missing, then we suspect that there's something going on in there that we haven't identified.

The best example of this that comes to mind is in radioactive decay. This is kind of like an alchemical change in which one type of atom changes, or decays, into another type of atom. What happens typically is that a fast electron, called a *beta particle*, that's measurable, comes out. However, there's always a tiny mass discrepancy, and there's also a discrepancy in spin. That was our first clue that there might be some overlooked type of particle, which was proposed by Pauli. He and Fermi called it the *neutrino* around 1930.

Now at that time, Bohr wasn't willing to countenance such a strange particle that would have no charge, no mass, but just a half unit of spin—that's it—and that would account for the energy going off. Instead, Bohr was willing to give up the principle of conservation of energy. He said that maybe on a subatomic level the principle of conservation of energy is just approximately obeyed. But most other physicists clung to the notion of conservation of energy. And by hanging on to that principle, they were able to deduce—not prove, mind you, just deduce—that there must be some other type of particle.

Now, it was more than 20 years after that—it wasn't until 1956—that the neutrino was actually shown to exist. So for 20 years there was a great deal of doubt as to whether the principle of conservation of energy even held at the quantum level or whether it was just a classic notion.

Now, the reason I'm bringing this up is that it may be that what New Age people are calling "energy" may in fact be some unusual kind of energy that we don't know about yet in ordinary physics. If that's the case then, there must be some kind of experiment we can do in which we do all of the bookkeeping on the energy flows involved, and low and behold, there's a little bit missing. Now, chances are that would be a difficult kind of experiment. But I'm just thinking that in principle, if these people are using the word energy in some way that relates to the physics of energy, then that's the sort of thing one would expect in the long run, however long the run is [*laughs*].

Saul-Paul Sirag is a theoretical physicist who has published papers on cosmology and unified field theory, most particularly on how these topics relate to consciousness. He studied theology at Prairie Bible Institute in Alberta. Subsequently, he went to UC Berkeley to study mathematics and physics. He served as president of the San Francisco Parapsychology Research Group between 1987 and 1989. He founded and led the Consciousness Theory Group (1977–1979) and was a seminar leader of the annual physics conferences at

Esalen, Big Sur, California (1978–1988). For many years, he has been working on a hyperspace theory of consciousness, based on the mathematics of the unification of the four known physical forces: electromagnetism, the weak and strong nuclear forces, and gravity. Sirag resides in Oregon with his wife.

Appendix C: Coming Soon to a Horse Near You

How to Find a Horse

According to the United Nations Global Horse Population report from 2014, our planet has an estimated 58,832,221 horses, 42,761,905 donkeys, 10,157,135 mules, and 755,000 zebras, bringing the total number of equines to 112,506,261. The United States is home to an estimated 10,260,000 equines, of whom 9.2 million are domesticated horses and 200,000 are horses who roam free on federal and tribal lands. Somewhere in those millions there is an Equine-imity horse for you!

Ideally, your Equine-imity activities will take place within a structured program in an equestrian school or in a center that provides therapeutic riding, hippotherapy, or equine-assisted learning and psychotherapy. If cost is an issue, you can often get stress-reducing horse time by volunteering at one of these centers. Most of them are nonprofit organizations that cherish their helpers and might give lessons in exchange for work.

Many private horse owners also have the knowledge and experience required for meeting, grooming, and leading as described in part IV. Some of them will additionally be skilled enough to guide you aboard their calm, gentle, child-safe horses at a standstill or give you a carefully contained pony ride–type meditation in an arena. You might trade horse and barn chores for instructional time. *Know your teachers and trust your instincts—do not play with a horse on the ground, much less on her back, if you lack confidence in the horse or her person that day. A horse who is safe and mellow on a hot, still day might become too amped up to be safe on a cold, gusty day.*

The following organizations and individuals, in alphabetical order, are among the top resources for horse activities. Their certified instructors, centers, and members are located in every state of the US, every province of Canada, and in Mexico, Europe, Asia, Australia, New Zealand, and South and Central America.

The **4-H Club** began in 1902 as the "The Tomato Club" or the "Corn Growing Club" and was synonymous with the teaching of animal and agricultural skills to youth. Although it has expanded to include rocketry, robotics, environmental protection, and computer science, many clubs are still focused on animals, including horses. Find a 4-H Club at https://4-h.org/find/

The **Certified Horsemanship Association** trains and certifies riding, carriage driving, and horsemanship instructors; trail guides, ranch operations managers, and vaulting coaches; and accredits equine teaching facilities and programs. Find a CHA-certified instructor at https://cha.horse/find-cha-professional-near-me/

Eagala (Equine Assisted Growth and Learning Association) is the premier organization worldwide for training and certifying equine-assisted learning and psychotherapy professionals.

Its website lists hundreds of certified providers in and outside the US. Find an EAGALA-certified provider at https://www.eagala.org/programs

Eponaquest, founded and directed by Linda Kohanov in Tucson, Arizona, certifies equine-facilitated learning instructors with emphasis on psychospiritual development. Linda wrote what is possibly the Bible of equine-facilitated psychospiritual development, *The Tao of Equus*. The Eponaquest website lists certified providers throughout the world. Find an Eponaquest-recommended instructor at https://eponaquest.com/recommended-instructors/

FFA began as Future Farmers of America, focused on farming and agriculture. Like 4-H, FFA has broadened its scope to include a range of other career pathways for future biologists, chemists, veterinarians, engineers, entrepreneurs, and leaders. Some of its programs still offer instruction with horses. Find an FFA Chapter at https://www.ffa.org/chapter-locator/

Horses & Pathfinders was founded and directed by Lucinda Newman in Moretown, VT. Lucinda is certified by SkyHorse Academy and is one of the pioneers of somatic horsemanship. http://horsesandpathfinders.com/

PATH International (Professional Association of Therapeutic Horsemanship) is the premier organization worldwide for training and certifying therapeutic riding and therapeutic carriage driving instructors and centers. Its website lists hundreds of certified centers and providers in and beyond the US. Find a PATH-certified center and instructor at https://www.pathintl.org/path-intl-centers/path-intl-centers

The Reflective Horse in Los Angeles, was founded and is directed by Cassandra Ogier. Cassandra is certified by SkyHorse EGE, is the creator of Somatic Riding, and is one of the pioneers of somatic horsemanship. http://www.thereflectivehorse.com/somatic-riding

SkyHorse Academy in Northern California, founded and directed by Ariana Strozzi Mazzucchi, trains and certifies equine-guided education facilitators with emphasis on Equine Guided Somatics and equine-guided coaching with a psychospiritual emphasis. Ariana can be considered the Goddess of Somatic Horsemanship and is one of the longest-standing professionals in equine-assisted activities. She is certified as a Master Somatic Coach by the Strozzi Institute. Find Ariana and her EGE-certified facilitators at https://www.skyhorseacademy.com

United States Pony Clubs is the largest equestrian education organization in the world. Find a Pony Club at https://www.ponyclub.org/FindPonyClub/Map.aspx

Here are suggestions for how to locate other organizations and individuals who offer instruction with horses:

1. Google "riding lessons," "equine-assisted learning," "equine experiential learning," "equine-facilitated learning," "equine-guided education," "somatic horsemanship," "equine-assisted somatic experiencing," "therapeutic riding," "horse therapy," "horse rescue," "trail rides," "riding vacations," "[your city] horses."
2. Look for horse boarding facilities in your area.
3. Look on bulletin boards in tack and feed stores.

4. Look online for your county horsemen's association.
5. Ask for referrals from a large-animal veterinary clinic.
6. Inquire at your local middle schools, high schools, colleges, and universities that offer rodeo and other equestrian programs.
7. Inquire at your local college of veterinary medicine.
8. Look in the course catalogs of your local colleges and universities.

Appendix D: EAATing
at the Grownup Table

Careers in Equine-Assisted
Activities and Therapies

If, in the course of Equine-imity, you become enamored of horses and horsemanship, you might be inspired to consider additional learning and service opportunities. Whether you are a high school or college student taking the first steps on your career path or someone starting a new path in midlife or retirement, it's never too early or too late to embark on a life with horses in equine-assisted activities and therapies (EAAT).

Acquiring training and competence in EAAT is a rewarding pursuit with numerous options. Choosing to work with horses and other equines promotes the survival and welfare of these animals and provides unique ways to help people.

The better-known careers with horses include veterinarian, farrier (shoer), riding instructor, breeder, and horse trainer. Becoming an equine vet requires academic excellence in science and math, an aptitude for medical and surgical procedures, years of schooling, terrific bedside manner, and a tolerance for frequent twenty-four-hour workdays. The requirements for the other professions are generally fewer but you will need the same amount of dedication, people skills, patience, and professionalism. In all walks of EAAT, the compensation is in the relationships, joy, and knowing you're making an important contribution, especially to the well-being of animals.

The Professional Association of Therapeutic Horsemanship (PATH, formerly NARHA, North American Riding for the Handicapped) defines EAAT as "any specific center-based activity, e.g., therapeutic riding, mounted or ground activities, grooming and stable management, shows, parades, demonstrations, etc., in which the center's clients, participants, volunteers, instructors and equines are involved."

Some lesser known, ultra-rewarding EAAT professions that even school guidance and career counselors might not be aware of are listed here.

Hippotherapy is physical therapy on horseback provided by a state-licensed physical therapist, occupational therapist, or speech/language pathologist. Hippotherapy patients typically have severe disabilities, often congenital, such as cerebral palsy and traumatic brain injury and other neuromuscular dysfunctions. The movement of the horse is therapeutic. During the intake examination, each patient is matched to a horse whose movement style will be the most beneficial for the patient's condition. Patients are then mounted and closely attended and do not generally attain the ability to ride independently.

The American Hippotherapy Association
https://www.americanhippotherapyassociation.org

Therapeutic Riding (TR)/Driving/Vaulting is also called adaptive riding. All three forms of therapy use both ground-work, such as grooming, and mounted or carriage activities conducted by certified therapeutic riding instructors for clients who have conditions such as musculo-skeletal injuries, autism spectrum disorders, stroke and other paralytic disorders, rheumatoid arthritis, multiple sclerosis, and chronic fatigue syndrome. TR clients are initially aided by a person leading the horse or driving the carriage and by one or two side walkers. Many clients are eventually able to ride or drive independently. Therapeutic carriage driving can accommodate clients in wheelchairs who are otherwise unable to ride.

Professional Association of Therapeutic Horsemanship International (PATH)
http://www.pathintl.org/

Equine-Assisted Psychotherapy (EAP) is performed mostly on the ground, sometimes mounted, by college-educated, board-certified, state-licensed professionals such as psychiatrists, clinical psychologists, marriage and family therapists, and clinical social workers. Typical patients or clients include individuals, couples, and families with post-traumatic stress disorder (PTSD), depression, chemical dependency/addiction, eating disorders; at-risk and delinquent youth; and victims of abuse or domestic violence. Nonviolent psychotic patients are sometimes accepted for contact with horses.

Equine Assisted Growth and Learning Association (Eagala)
http://www.eagala.org/

Equine-guided learning, coaching, personal development, and spiritual care provides groundwork and mounted activities presented as private sessions, workshops, and seminars for individuals, couples, families, and business or community groups. Sessions are conducted by EAP professionals, life coaches, educators, clergy and other spiritual counselors, human resources specialists, and self-designated lay practitioners. Typical clients are those needing assistance with stress reduction, business development, traumatic experiences, life transitions, and psychospiritual growth. If you are researching this field, you will also see it referred to as equine-assisted learning (EAL), equine-facilitated learning, equine experiential learning, equine guided education, and similar terms.

See Eagala above
Eponaquest Worldwide
http://eponaquest.com/

Somatic Horsemanship emphasizes the physical relationship with horses. Equine-imity somatic horsemanship is additionally a form of body-centered equine-guided somato-psycho-spiritual learning. Other somatic horsemanship practices include equine-assisted Somatic Experiencing, equine-assisted EMDR (Eye Movement Desensitization and Reprocessing), yoga on horseback, and tai ji on horseback.

SkyHorse Academy
https://www.skyhorseacademy.com

EQUSSOMA
Trauma-Focused Equine-Assisted Somatic Experiencing
https://equusoma.com

College Degree Programs

As of this writing, few colleges offer degrees in equine-assisted learning and psychotherapy per se. The usual route is to pursue general professional education, certification, and licensure in psychology, social work, coaching, body work, or a health-related field like medicine, nursing, or physical therapy, and then obtain special training in an EAAT program.

The following is a representative list of training and certification programs and organizations with which I have had personal, positive experiences.

Carroll College
Helena, Montana
Anthrozoology with equine studies emphasis; the first degree program of its kind in the US
https://www.carroll.edu/anthrozoology/equine-classes

Prescott College
Prescott, Arizona
Undergraduate and graduate programs and certification in Equine Assisted Mental Health
https://www.prescott.edu/equine-assisted-mental-health

Texas Tech University
Lubbock, Texas
Equine Science Program
https://www.depts.ttu.edu/afs/horse/docs/Equine_Certifi-
cate_.pdf

Non-degree Training and Certification Programs
in alphabetical order

American Hippotherapy Association
http://www.americanhippotherapyassociation.org/

Eagala (Equine Assisted Growth and Learning Association)
EAL/P—UNtrainings throughout the US, Europe, Asia,
Pacific, and South Africa
http://www.eagala.org/

Equine Experiential Education Association (E3A)
Corporate teams-oriented EAL
https://e3assoc.org

Eponaquest Worldwide
Corporate, psychospiritual, and somatic EAL
http://eponaquest.com/

Gestalt Equine Institute of the Rockies
Littleton, Colorado
http://www.gestaltequineinstitute.com

PATH (Professional Association of Therapeutic Horsemanship International)
Therapeutic riding, driving, and vaulting
http://www.pathintl.org/

SkyHorse Academy Equine-Assisted Learning
Somatic horsemanship internships and basic and continuing education
https://www.skyhorseacademy.com

Volunteer and Other Local Opportunities

Search the internet using the name of your town or county using any of the EAAT terms above.

GLOSSARY

aikido "eye kee doe." Literally, the Way of Blending Energy. Ki is *qi* (*ch'i*) and do is *Dao*. A martial art performed with a partner, also called an opponent.

archetype. A concept developed by Carl Jung to indicate parts of the psyche that are prominent in myths and dreams. Archetypes are what are projected onto others. See **projection** and **somarchetype**.

Ba Duan Jin. A set of eight *qigong* forms that has been studied extensively for health benefits in stress and cancer treatment. See *Wu Duan Jin*.

back to grazing. The horse's ability to quickly recover from a traumatic event.

bank robber's knot. A looped, not knotted way of tying horses that releases with a single pull on the free end of the rope.

bodymind. The integration of one's physical, mental, emotional, and intuitive functions as one spiritually holistic unit. See **Four Ways of Wisdom**.

Bubbling Springs. Energy centers located behind the balls of the feet between the second and third toes. The Kidney

1 point on the acupuncture **meridians**. Used for creating a connection to the earth and **grounding** one's energy.

canter. The horse's moderately fast three-beat gait, also called a lope in Western riding.

ch'i. Older, easier to pronounce version of *qi*, the universal life force.

corral. A fenced pen that holds one or more horses. Other than the small, portable models, a corral is generally larger than a **paddock**, smaller than a pasture.

curry comb. A semi-hard grooming tool that massages the horse's skin and loosens dirt.

dan tien "dahn tyen." One of three main energy centers located around the third eye (upper dan tien), the heart (middle dan tien), and below the navel (lower dan tien). Unless otherwise specified, it refers to the lower energy center, the seat of power and conviction.

dan tien breathing. "Belly breathing." Deep, stress-relief breathing that expands the abdomen. An antidote for rapid, shallow, anxious breathing that only expands the upper chest.

dan tien hug. A relaxing energy and breathing interaction with a horse in which the human faces the horse's front with one arm on the horse's back and nestles close to the horse's belly.

dan tien press. A relaxing energy and breathing interaction with a horse in which the human puts both hands on the horse's body, facing the horse's side.

Dao. An ancient Chinese philosophical concept meaning the Great Emptiness or the Way. See *wu ji*.

EAAT:Equine-Assisted Activities and Therapies. Includes **hippotherapy, therapeutic riding, equine-guided learning**

and psychotherapy, **somatic horsemanship**, and conventional riding lessons.

embodiment. The state of being in a physical body. Manifestation of abstract qualities by a physical body. "Horses are the embodiment of wellness."

energy. See **putative energy** and **veritable energy**.

energy medicine. The use of **putative energies**, such as ch'i and ki, for healing. Related practices include laying on of hands.

entrainment. The process by which one system's motion or signal frequency exerts a synchronization effect on the frequency of another system. Examples are entrainment of the heart rate or brain waves between two or more individuals. In Equine-imity, the entrainment of an anxious human's rapid heart rate to a relaxed horse's lower heart rate.

epiphenomenalism. The belief that all mental processes, and consciousness itself, can be reduced to and predicted by neurochemical phenomena in the physical brain cells. The belief that consciousness resides in and comes from the brain.

equanimity. Calmness, composure, and evenness of temper, especially in a difficult situation.

equine-assisted learning. Activities with horses for individuals, groups, and families. Also known as equine-guided education, equine-facilitated learning, equine experiential education, and similar combinations of those terms.

equine-assisted psychotherapy. Services provided by licensed mental health professionals, in partnership with horses and equine professionals, to treat psychological conditions that might ordinarily be addressed in an office practice.

Equine-imity. A somatic horsemanship program developed at Stanford Medical School by Beverley Kane, MD. The word is a play on **equanimity**.

feral. An animal whose ancestors were, or who himself was, once domesticated but now lives independently from humans. Most horses worldwide are either feral on public lands or domesticated on farms and ranches. See **wild**.

fight-or-flight response. A response to stress mediated by the sympathetic nervous system in which the animal either runs away or does battle. The response is accompanied by an outpouring of the stress hormones adrenalin and cortisol. See **rest and digest**.

Four Ways of Wisdom. Based on the teachings of twentieth-century Swiss psychiatrist Carl Jung, refers to the balance of the four types of intelligence: intellectual, emotional (feeling), somatic (physical, sensory), and intuitive (instinctual).

Gassho "gah-show." A gesture in which the hands are held at heart level as if praying. It means "hands together" in Japanese. In yoga, called *anjali mudra*. Used as the closing gesture in each of the *Wu Duan Jin* forms.

gelding. Castrated male horse.

General Adaptation Syndrome. The name given by Hans Selye (1907–1982) to describe the physiological changes in the body when faced with a physical or psychological stressor. The syndrome includes release of adrenalin, cortisol, and other stress hormones and neurotransmitters.

grounding. Feeling one's energy going down into the earth, especially using the **Bubbling Springs**. A technique for imagining that one is draining out unpleasant sensations from an overactive mind and overwrought emotions.

Guo Lin New Qigong. A set of *qigong* forms that has been studied extensively for health benefits in cancer treatment. Originated by Guo Lin, a Chinese woman with ovarian cancer who survived for twenty years longer than predicted by conventional medicine.

head-shy. Descriptor of a horse who does not like touching or objects around his head. Often due to a history of traumatic incidents, such as slapping or harsh bridling, involving the head.

hippotherapy. Physical therapy on horseback provided by certified physical therapists, physiatrists, occupational therapists, and speech pathologists.

individuation. The process, named by Carl Jung, by which all the archetypes are integrated into the Whole Self.

Inner Smile. A gesture in which we smile inwardly to all organs in the body and feel them smiling back. The Inner Smile meditation activates the energy of loving-kindness, especially toward oneself.

ki "kee." Japanese for qi/ch'i, the life force energy.

kinesthetic empathy. The ability to experience sensations in one's own body by observing the movements or physical condition of another being or object.

liberty horse. A horse who is not tethered to a fixed object or being held on a lead rope. The horse is free to move about at will, and away from humans, within the limits of her pasture, corral, paddock, or stall.

longeing "lunj-ing." Asking the horse to move around in a circle at any or all of the three gaits: walk, trot, and **canter**. Usually done in a twenty-meter round arena with a leash and a long stick—"line longeing"—or with the arms and a short stick—"free longeing." Used to exercise a non-pastured horse, test for lameness, and experiment with ch'i and body language.

mare. Female horse.

Masterson Method. Stress- and injury-relieving equine body work developed by Jim Masterson using massage along meridians and in other areas. See also **Tellington Touch**.

medical *qigong*. Qigong used in modern medical settings for healing mental and physical illness. The qigong sets most studied using gold-standard medical research methods are the *Ba Duan Jin*, the Five Animal (or Five Elements) Frolics, and *Guo Lin New Qigong*.

meridians. In energy medicine, especially acupuncture, channels in which *ch'i* flows.

mind-body dualism. The belief that mental properties and physical properties are fundamentally different, that the mind and brain are separate. René Descartes taught that the mind is the seat of consciousness and the physical brain is the seat of intelligence. See **epiphenomenalism**.

mindfulness. Focusing on the present moment with unclouded, nonjudgmental awareness. Filtering out distractions, extraneous thoughts, and worries to appreciate the now.

mirror neurons. Brain cells, or a network of cells, that fire both when an animal acts and when the animal observes the same action performed by another. See **somarchetypal projection**.

natural horsemanship. A gentle way of training and treating horses, in contrast with cruel measures that were used to "break" horses on ranches in the nineteenth century.

non-transitive dominance hierarchy. A pecking order in which if A is dominant to B and B is dominant to C, C might still be dominant to A in some situations.

paddock. Horse's fenced living quarters that usually includes a stall or shed open on one side to a dirt yard area. Usually housing a single horse, paddocks vary greatly in size from 15 x 15 feet to 50 x 50 feet or more. See **stall** and **corral**.

pre-sentience or presentiment. The body's ability to perceive a sensory event before it happens, as described by Dean Radin of the Institute of Noetic Sciences, Rollin McCraty of HeartMath, and others.

projection. The act of attributing or blaming one's internal traits to or on living beings or inanimate objects outside the self. See **archetypes** and **somarchetypes**.

psychological types. Carl Jung's classification of the main functional divisions of consciousness—thinking, sensing, feeling (emotions), and intuiting. Each function is further characterized by traits of extraversion and introversion. See **Four Ways of Wisdom**.

Push Hands. A *tai ji* practice performed facing a partner, using the hands, wrists, and arms and lunging gently back and forth. Teaches energy blending and shared leadership.

putative energy. Defined by the National Center for Complementary and Integrative Health as energy, like ch'i and reiki, whose effects can be observed and measured but that themselves can't be measured. See **veritable energy**.

qi "chee." The universal life force found in all beings and objects. *Ki* ("ki") in Japanese.

qigong "chee goong." An ancient Chinese moving meditation used for health benefits.

qigong, **medical**. See **medical** *qigong*.

rei ki. Spirit **ki** or spiritual energy.

Reiki. A method of healing with **putative energy** developed by Japanese Buddhist monk Mikao Usui in the nineteenth century.

rest and digest (also called rest and replenish). A state of relaxation mediated by the parasympathetic nervous system. Can be deliberately activated when under stress or as a pre-sponse to (preparation for) stress using meditation techniques. Also called the feed-and-breed state. See **fight-or-flight response**.

shy. A horse's mild reaction to a scary object or situation. Usually manifests as a small hop or a veering away from the offending article. See **spook**.

6 Ms of grooming. Mechanical, Medical, Mood, Manners, Melding, Meditation.

soft eyes. A way of seeing, described by Centered Riding pioneer Sally Swift, in which one's vision is simultaneously centrally focused and peripherally aware. A meditation of the eyes.

somarchetypal projection. Imagined sensations of the physical characteristics that one hopes or fears she may possess, triggered by seeing another person's or animal's physique or actions. See **mirror neurons, projection**.

somarchetype. A somatic archetype of characteristic physical attributes—fatness, thinness, baldness, strength, tallness, shortness—that is projected onto others who have those characteristics. See **archetype, projection**, and **somarchetypal projection**.

somatic "so MAT ik." Pertaining to the physical body, its anatomy and physiology.

somatic horsemanship. The art of relating to horses using heightened awareness of one's own and the horse's physical bodies.

somatopathic. Empathy felt by the body. The ability to sense what another person or animal's body is sensing. See **mirror neurons**.

spook. A horse's strong reaction to a scary object or situation. May manifest as a sudden sideways jump, running, or rearing. See **shy**.

stall. A horse's walled living quarters, in the US, typically 12 x 12 feet, usually in a barn. See **paddock** and **corral**.

stall vices. Behaviors such as swaying back and forth, chewing on wood, pawing the ground, and kicking the walls that usually indicate a horse's stress from boredom.

stress response. See General Adaptation Syndrome.

tack. Saddles, saddle pads, bridles, halters, lead ropes, and similar equipment.

tai ji. A Daoist concept meaning the Great Polarity, the state of the universe just after Creation where *yin* and *yang* appear and polarize eachother. See *Dao* and *wu ji*. Also the martial art that is practiced as both a gentle, moving meditation and as a combat sport.

Tellington Touch (TTouch). Stress and injury-relieving equine body work developed by Linda Tellington-Jones using gentle massage. Also for dogs, cats, and humans. See also **Masterson Method**.

tethering. Tying or holding a horse so as to limit her voluntary movement. See **liberty horse**.

therapeutic riding. A service offered by certified therapeutic riding instructors to mentally and physically disabled persons who benefit from ground activities and riding (or carriage driving or vaulting). See **hippotherapy**.

Traditional Chinese Medicine (TCM). A set of ancient and modern philosophies and practices that include acupuncture, *qigong*, and herbal remedies.

trot. The horse's two-beat gait. May be slow or fast. The slower trot in Western riding is called a jog.

turnout. Taking the horse out of her stall or paddock into a larger space for exercise or socializing. Maximizing turnout time each day promotes optimum health. Horses who live in a pasture are turned out 24/7.

tying, blocker. Tethering a horse to a metal blocker tie ring that uses a magnetic clasp.

tying, cross. Tethering a horse, usually hard tied, using ropes clipped to both sides of her halter.

tying, ground. Tethering a horse to her trained habit of remaining in place when the lead rope or reins are dropped to the ground.

tying, hard. Tethering a horse to a metal ring or post from which she cannot break loose.

tying, soft. Tethering a horse to a string or bush from which she can break loose.

veritable energy. Defined by the National Center for Complementary and Integrative Health as energy, like electric current and calories, that can be measured. See **putative energy**.

visual field. The area that can be seen by the eyes when the head is held stationary.

wild (animal). An animal whose lineage has never been domesticated. The last true wild horse breed is the rare and endangered Przewalski ("sha-VAHL-skee") horse native to the Mongolian steppes. See **feral**.

Wu Duan Jin. A five-form subset of the *Ba Duan Jin* that can be performed on horseback. Here, *wu* means "five."

wu ji. A Daoist concept meaning the Great Emptiness. The universe before Creation. Literally, no polarity. Here, *wu* means "not" or "no thing." See *Dao* and *tai ji*.

yang. The masculine principle characterized as assertive, light, hot, hard, dry, expanding, inhaling. Not necessarily pertaining to males or men.

yin. The feminine principle characterized as receptive, dark, cold, soft, wet, contracting, exhaling. Not necessarily pertaining to females or women.

Illustration Credits

Cover

Montage by Judith Ogus. Background:
  © Shutterstock.com /Alesikka; Horses by Xu Beihong
  (1895–1953); bamboo: iStock.com/JY Lee

Pages 2, 34, 80, 148: iStock.com/JY Lee

7   Visual fields of the horse. Adapted from Gerrit Riet-
veld. Used with permission.

9   *Green Pastures*. Licensed Image:
Bonnie Mason/Pixels.com

13   Native American warrior. iStock.com/Daniel Eskridge

16   Top: Four knights on horseback. Rider-Waite Tarot
Bottom: Native American medicine wheel.
iStock.com/kroecker

22   Chiron Centaur. Wellcome Collection

35   "Does this saddle …?" Ian Culley.
http://www.mighty-pencil.com.
Used with permission.

40   Venus of Willendorf. Wikimedia Creative Commons,
courtesy of Matthias Kabel.

66   Yerkes-Dodson Law graph.
      Judith Ogus randomarts.biz

78   Talula rolling. Photo by Elizabeth Sullivan.

82   MaJiaYao culture pottery vessel. Courtesy of Prof.
      Gary Lee Todd, Sias International Univ., Henan,
      China.

82   Hua Tuo and the monkey.
      Wikimedia Creative Commons.

87   Yin and yang horses. Arabian horse logo courtesy of
      Maggie Macnab, ©1985 Maggie Macnab and Bureau
      of Land Management. All rights reserved.

89   Xing Qi Ming jade cylinder. Inscription on Guiding
      Ch'i. Warring States Period, 475–221 BCE.

91   *Green Energy.* iStock.com/Beboy_ltd.

99   Master Yanran on Jake. Photo by Ruben Kleiman.

101   Ch'i and Reiki: Reiki gong Chinese script.
      yellowbridge.com

105   Water wheel, Mill Creek Vineyards, Healdsburg, CA.
      Photo by Ruben Kleiman.

113   Wu ji circle. Oleksandr Kashcheiev © 123RF.com

115   Yin and yang symbol. Ink and Gossip
      Illustration Transparent Decorative.

117   Bubbling Springs foot center. iStock/karelnoppe.

119   Left: Author on Basia. Photo by Ruben Kleiman.
      Right: Stirrup over Bubbling Springs.
      Judith Ogus randomarts.biz

124   Earth and Sky Reiki Cleanse.
      Photos by Ruben Kleiman.

126   Gassho/Anjali mudra. iStock.com/Khosrork

127 Open and Close. Photos by Ruben Kleiman.

Wu Duan Jin monks. Traditional, artist unknown:

   134   Hold Up the Sky.
   137   Shoot the Arrow.
   140   Separate Heaven and Earth.
   141   Wise Old Owl Looks Around.
   142   Punch With an Angry Gaze.

Author exercise photos by Ruben Kleiman:

   136   Hold Up the Sky.
   138   Shoot the Arrow.
   145   Punch with an Angry Gaze.

172 Dan tien press, Sasha and Lokin.
    Photo by Beverley Kane.

175 Dan tien hug, author and Rhett.
    Photo by Ruben Kleiman.

178 Horses Grooming Eachother. Courtesy of Debra
    Feinman Photography/debrafeinman.com

187 Blocker tie ring. Toklat Originals.

189 Bank robber's knot. Photos by Ruben Kleiman.

190 Curry comb. Weatherbeeta USA Inc.

193 Hoof pick. Weatherbeeta USA Inc.

200 Pablo Picasso, *Boy Leading Horse*, 1906. Oil on canvas.
    The William S. Paley Collection. NY MOMA © ARS,
    NY.

213 Stanford Equine-imity meditation ride.
    Photo by Beverley Kane.

220 Talula's happiest trail, Webb Ranch. Photos by Beverley Kane. Montage by Judith Ogus. randomarts.biz

295 Author. Photo by Elizabeth Sullivan.

asshos of gratitude for everyone who helped *Equine-imity* emerge from the Nothingness. All I have done and learned has culminated in this book. So here I acknowledge the many diverse, longtime, and more recent contributors to this finale.

Equine-imity is dedicated to Ruben Kleiman, Renaissance man, husband, and best friend of thirty-three years. Ruben unreservedly, unstintingly, uncritically supported my transition from clinical physician to medical informaticist to horse sensei. He gave his all for this book. All his love, all his creativity, all his Photoshop finesse; the fruits of all his years in linguistics, literary criticism, physics, philosophy, and hermeneutics. Ruben's sunny nature shone into the dark depths of my writer's block and self-suspected suckiness. He supported me intellectually with constructive criticism as the sincerest form of flattery. He supported me somatically with hugs, tea, and gourmet dinners. He meticulously edited multiple iterations, dozens of drafts, over *Equine-imity's* eight years of false starts and final stabs. One of my colleagues has a couples workshop called What If Your Husband Were a Horse? It teaches people to be as kind, compassionate, and patient with their spouses as they are with their horses. May I always be so for Ruben.

I am grateful for the innovative programming of, and enthusiastic promotion by, the Stanford Health Improvement Program (HIP). Stanford provided both the stress that brought my students to class and the educational stipends for its tuition. Years ago, it was my great good fortune to be introduced to Laurie Ausserer, then HIP's Health Education Program Director. Remembering the horses she had while growing up, Laurie immediately and totally got the vision for Equine-imity. She gave us the Go, Nellie the moment she dismounted from the meditation ride, 7 November, 2012. Thanks and praise to Laurie's successor, Dominque Del Chiaro, for continued support and for always remembering to bring me in from the back forty for continuing education with other HIP providers.

Stanford's Medicine and the Muse program, directed by Professor of Anesthesiology Audrey Shafer, is a goddess-send to the medical humanities. In conjunction with that program, I have been inspired and incentivized by support from Pegasus, our Stanford Physician Writers Group. Pegasus Group Five members Diana Faird, Andy Grose, and Richard Mamelok were especially perceptive, deft, and encouraging. Thank you to Stanford Medical Writer-in-Residence and best-selling author, Laurel Braitman, who truly understands the writer's woe of ecstasy.

I offer eighteen years of accumulated and insufficiently expressed appreciation to Summer Hubbard Hensley, my riding instructor, who took me on as a new rider when I was fifty-two. Classically trained but untainted by the mishegoss of fads and fallacies in the equestrian world, Summer was the first manifestation of the Triple Goddess of Horsemanship archetype. Her wisdom, patience, and professionalism—and innate understanding of mind-body riding—astonish me every Thursday at noon. I am also grateful to my other trainers: Summer's mom, Lyndal Webb Hubbard, and her mantra for spooky horses, "No big deal"; crusty cowgirl with a heart of gold Joan McLaren; our dedicated quadrille coach, Sharon Wormhoudt; and my friend, three-time World Endurance Champion and heiress to Sally Swift Centered Riding, Becky Hart.

Equine-imity would still be stuck in the wu ji without Corie Thompson, another manifestation of the Triple Horse Goddess. When I was three-legged lame, the Fates chose Corie as my therapeutic riding instructor at the National Center for Equine Facilitated Therapy. Corie's ten-page booklet for the NCEFT program for veterans with PTSD grew into the Equine-imity syllabus, which grew into this book. Corie became my first Equine-imity co-facilitator, a joy to work with, and now a joy to ride with at Webb. In recent years, Robin Murphy has been my energetic, conscientious, and skilled PATH-certified co-facilitator. Robin's infectious joy is like a tonic to employees trudging wearily over to Webb from Stanford. When Robin goes camping in the wilderness, I have been grateful for co-facilitation by Françoise Vincent, Shannon Fitzgibbon, Marie Hudson, Miriam Tidmarsh, and Kassi Lobner.

Thanks to the hundreds of Equine-imity, qigong, and tai ji students who shared their dedication, commitment, insights, and inner processes with me and with eachother. Chief among them, I thank Vera Shadle, who always volunteered for new activities and new horses; Elayne Weissler-Martello, who asked probing and thoughtful questions; and the late DeeDee (Maejong) Johnson Zawayeh, who loved Silver and taught me how deeply horses heal us. Thanks especially to those students who did all of the above plus beta tested the manuscript: psychologist Joe Fama and Stanford Engineering

School technical documentation editor Mary McDevitt. Gassho for thoughtful comments from friends and colleagues Sondra Barrett, Sheri Bortz, Lucia Mokres, and Elizabeth Sullivan. Dean Radin kindly took time from his busy schedule at the Institute of Noetic Sciences to answer my questions about his work. I enjoyed our discussions of presentience over email and at Russ Targ's birthday party.

The third manifestation of the Triple Horse Goddess is the conjoined spirits of my sisters in somatic horsemanship, Ariana Strozzi Mazzucchi and Cassandra Ogier. Our bareback rides and bared souls, the latter under the influence of Ariana's excellent homemade wine, confirmed our shared values of sensory joy, integrity, congruency, and authenticity.

Since 2004, the Webb Ranch, now in operation almost one hundred years, has generously supported my students, clients, workshops, and ventures. I am especially grateful to Webb management, Tom and Lyndal Hubbard and Nate and Summer Hensley, for sustenance during this difficult year. All through the pandemic, which continues at this writing, Webb has been our sanity and salvation as we continue to walk the land and care for our horses.

Dan tien hugs to our more than one hundred magnificent Webb lesson horses. I am filled with joy each time one of them volunteers to come over to meet and greet us in pasture; to my first horse, Dream; to my first fifty-mile endurance mount, Deuce (Blind Faith) Wonders; to Codigh (Cody), who taught me what spookiness means; to Smarty, who taught me what bombproof means; to Jasper, who gave me the biggest belly laugh with his canter-to-halt transition and green broke me of overthinking my riding. And especially to Talula-Serena, with whom I have the deepest, longest, most ongoing, learning and loving relationship.

Although Equine-imity, with its mounted activities, departs from the Eagala model, Eagala UNtrainings and the SPUD'S paradigm have been fundamental to all my work. For this I am indebted to former Eagala founders and directors Greg Kirsten, Lynn Thomas, and Mickey DiGiacomo. I am grateful for initiation into equine-facilitated learning, periodic communication, and lasting inspiration from Barbara Rector and Linda Kohanov. I value the clinical training Codigh and I had with Mark Rashid and Crissi McDonald, who also generously livestreamed many long Q&A sessions from their cozy ranch home, with views of the snowy Rockies, during the pandemic.

Thanks to Liz Carey, my best riding buddy and erstwhile Medicine and Horsemanship co-facilitator. Blessings upon our official Woodside Horse Shaman and personal friend, Morningstar*, who guided me in honoring her Native American horse traditions.

Deep bows to my senseis in tai ji, qigong, healing arts, and Eastern philosophy. Grand Master Li Shu Dong was my first teacher, whose powerful yet silken tai ji and qigong movements I have never seen equaled. I forgive and even thank him for abruptly pressing me into taking over his Stanford Medical Tai Chi class when he was appointed as member-at-large to the Chinese Health Ministry. Gratitude to Master Yanran and Master Hengyuan of the Shaolin Temple USA; to Paul Lam and the Tai Chi for Health Institute, including Robin Malby and Hong Yang. Hong infuses tai ji with an almost esoteric yet accessible somatic Daoism. She has deepened my understanding, teaching, and personal practice and confirmed many of Equine-imity's somato-spiritual principles. I am honored to know and practice with Lily Li, who tries valiantly, and I fear fruitlessly, to perfect my Lazy About Tying Coat. I am profoundly indebted to, with deep affection for, Dr. Alex Feng and Gideon Enz, Traditional Chinese Medical practitioners who tutored me privately in qigong and tai ji, restoring my health and ushering in my recovery from excess Liver Wind.

I heap thanks and praise on my wonderful editor and designer respectively, Sheridan McCarthy and Stanton Nelson, of Meadowlark Publishing Services. Sheridan was my shepherd, I did not want—for guidance, cheerleading, respect, and willingness to corral this runaway herd of multiple disciplines into a coherent whole. I appreciate Sheridan's flexibility with my often unconventional and controversial ideas. Thanks to friend, artist, and champion endurance rider Judith Ogus for her deft and creative—and fast!—renderings of my sparks of visual imagination. Thanks to publicist and marketing consultant David Ivester, who is seeing to the seeding and succeeding of our project. Thank you, eagle-eye proofreader Amy Thorne and sensitive indexer Susan Block.

Seeking out silver linings, I have been grateful to the Silicon Valley dotcom bust of 2001 that closed one door and opened another door—to horses; to Kokopelli the Trickster, who bucked me off the stepstool and tossed me twisted and broken into therapeutic riding. The many tragedies and hardships notwithstanding but not forgotten, I acknowledge the silver lining in the covid-19 pandemic. After years of delays and distractions, shelter-in-place became write-in-place. My asymptotic approach to completion of this book was fed by always learning something new to add after each Equine-imity session. This input ceased with Stanford's 2020 moratorium on classes.

Once again, bows and bear hugs for Ruben, the alpha and omega of acknowledgees, of the existence of this book, and of me.

INDEX

Bolded page numbers indicate glossary definitions
f following page number indicates footnote (e.g., 101*f*)

creating relationships, 152, 166

in equine-assisted therapies, 26, 76, 96

experienced horse people vs. beginners, 154–156

grooming and. *See* grooming

in Haunted House/UNin-formed consent, 154–156

human incongruencies, 4–5

leading and. *See* leading horses

round pen, crucible of rela-tionship, 157–159

softness and feel, 153–154

The Relaxation Response (Ben-son), 73–74

Releases and Gathers table, 142

releasing pressure, 158

religious view of physical body, 34–37

respect, 156, 201–203

rest and digest (rest and replenish), 61, **258**

rewarding the tiny try (positive reinforcement), 151–152

Rhett, the horse, 171

Rice, Jerry, 46

riding instructors, 20, 210–211, 243, 245

Roberts, Jane, 35

ropes. *See* leading horses; lead ropes; tying

Rosie, the horse, 66–67

round pens, 147, 157–159

routine, importance of, 65–66, 69, 179, 183, 186

Ruben (Kleiman), vii, 23, 168, 267, 272, 279

photo credits, 264–265

sacking out, 155*f*

sadness, 10, 142, 210

Separate Heaven and Earth for, 136–137

safety and etiquette, 164–165

Saint-Exupéry, Antoine de, 206

Sandy, the mule, 95–96

Sapolsky, Robert M., 57–58

Schechter, Bill, 198

Scott, Sylvia, 150

Selye, Hans, 57

sensation, as Jungian function, 43, 45

sensations, 60 *See also* Four Ways of Wisdom

and ch'i, 92

in animals, 44*f*, 48

from horses, 23, 187

and somarchetypes, 19

as symbols, 63

sensory perception, 20. *See also* kinesthetic empathy

Separate Heaven and Earth— Form 3

benefits of, 136

steps for performing, 136–137

Serena, the horse. *See* Talula.

Seth, 147

Shadle, Vera, 269

Shafer, Audrey, 268

shamans, 40, 80, 101

Shaolin monks, 85, 91, 96, 271

shape-shifting, 40, 80

Sheldrake, Rupert, 50

Shi De Yang (Shi Wanfeng), 122

shoes

for horses, 189, 243

for humans, 110, 164

Shoot the Arrow—Form 2

benefits of, 133

illustrations for, 134

steps for performing, 133, 135

About the Author

Beverley Kane, MD, is Adjunct Assistant Clinical Professor of Medicine at Stanford. She is Program Director for *Equine-imity* and Stanford *Medicine and Horsemanship*. She is also the course director and instructor for Stanford *Medical Tai Chi*, which includes the practice of both tai ji and qigong. Dr. Kane was previously Board Certified in Tai Chi for Energy by the Tai Chi for Health Institute. She is a Certified Horsemanship Association Level 1 riding instructor. Her private practice website is Horsensei Equine-Assisted Learning & THerapy (HEALTH) http://www.horsensei.com. She lives on the San Francisco Peninsula with her husband, Ruben, and cats, Kushami and Shénah.

Printed in the USA
CPSIA information can be obtained
at www.ICGtesting.com
LVHW060512201123
764349LV00023B/1498